S0-DZK-331

WHY SMASH ATOMS?

LONDON : GEOFFREY CUMBERLEGE
OXFORD UNIVERSITY PRESS

Official Photo U. S. A. A. F.

Smoke billows up over Nagasaki, Japan, after bombing by atomic bomb.

WHY SMASH ATOMS?

BY

ARTHUR K. SOLOMON

Research Fellow in Physics and Chemistry
Harvard University
Staff Member, Radiation Laboratory
Massachusetts Institute of Technology

Illustrated by

KATHERINE CAMPBELL DUFF

CAMBRIDGE, MASSACHUSETTS
HARVARD UNIVERSITY PRESS
1946

PRINTED IN THE UNITED STATES OF AMERICA

PREFACE TO THE REVISED EDITION

THE atomic bomb has resulted from the magnificent co-operation of a large group of people, including the Army, industry, and scientists. Deepest congratulations should be extended to that group of physicists who have so ably discharged the heavy burden which lay upon them in its development and production.

The new material which has been added to form the three new chapters in this book is derived from the Smyth report, to which has been added material from articles published in technical journals before the war, and certain information taken from newspaper accounts of the effects of the bomb.

J. R. Oppenheimer is the only working scientist mentioned by name in the new chapters who had not previously been introduced in the book. No other names have been included because the published information is too scanty to make it possible to allocate credit on any fair basis.

When I left England in January of this year, the proofs of the English edition of the book were not available. I am grateful to Mrs. I. Mathison for carrying out the tiresome task of reading them, and preparing the index of that edition.

In this new edition the pictorial material has been considerably revised and enlarged. Fritz Goro has given much sound advice in the editing of all the pictures, and *Life* has been gracious enough to allow me to reproduce many of Mr. Goro's own photographs. Unfortunately some of the English historical pictures, including those of Aston, Rutherford, Moseley, and Thomson, have come from a source which is now unknown, so they cannot be credited properly. My thanks are due to Dr. M. G. White and Dr. L. A. Turner for their criticism of the new material, and to Mr. William Laurence, of the New York *Times,* for permission to quote from his fine description of the atomic bomb explosion in New Mexico. Captain John Slocum has helped me particularly in the procurement of Army photographs. Julian Mack has given permission to use a caption taken from a letter in *Time.* Thanks are due the Press Association, Acme, Black Star, Keystone View Co., and the U. S. Army Air Forces and Signal Corps for permission to use their photographs.

A. K. SOLOMON

CAMBRIDGE, MASSACHUSETTS
OCTOBER, 1945

PREFACE TO THE FIRST EDITION

THIS book is the outcome of innumerable arguments in which I have had to defend my profession because many of my friends could not understand the practical purpose of smashing atoms. In the book I have tried to make clear my feeling that the purpose of smashing atoms is not only the practical applications which arise as by-products; but also and more important, the deeper understanding that comes with increasing knowledge.

But I do not want to give the impression that I work at my profession because it is practical. That would be putting the cart before the horse. I am a scientist because it is fun, because I have the opportunity of doing the things I like to do. If I felt that what I did was of no importance and that smashing atoms was my personal retreat into a less than ivory tower, I should soon cease to find it fun. Only as long as I am satisfied that the work is necessary can I enjoy myself putting in the long hours and the hard work that science demands.

To me it is important to stress that modern science is a coöperative phenomenon. Within physics itself, especially in machines the size of cyclotrons, the work can no longer be done by a single man. In spite of this, I have deliberately omitted the names of many whose work is fundamental to nuclear physics, not because I do not appreciate the value of their contributions, but for the more practical reason that too many names would confuse the reader.

One of the pleasures of writing a preface is that it provides an opportunity of acknowledging my indebtedness to a number of my friends, especially Professors G. B. Kistiakowsky, K. T. Bainbridge, and A. B. Hastings who are responsible for the opportunities that have led to the publication of this book. I want to express my thanks to Lord Rutherford for permission to work at the Cavendish Laboratory, and to Professor J. D. Cockcroft for his kind interest after Lord Rutherford's death. Building a cyclotron in Cambridge, England, would have been impossible without Dr. D. G. Hurst, R. Latham, and Dr. A. E. Kempton who incidentally led me gently from chemistry into physics; as well as C. G. Tilley who is responsible for teaching me how to use my hands. Mrs. C. V. Wintour has helped with the manuscript, and Harvey Brooks with his welcome and valuable criticisms of the whole book. Dr. Joseph Aub has given constructive advice on the medical chapter. Finally, I want to express my deepest appreciation to Katherine Campbell, for her intelligent understanding in devising the illustrations, and to G. Armour Craig and Professor Bainbridge, without whose kind but ruthless criticism the book would not have reached its present state.

I want to thank the Cambridge University Press for permission to reproduce my articles from *Discovery*, as well as R. Aves, Dr. D. Cooksey, Dr. H. R. Crane, Dr. A. J. Dempster, P. Donaldson, Dr. J. R. Dunning, Miss M. Shields, Dr. L. P. Smith, Dr. Van Atta, the Franklin Institute, and the General Electric Company for their assistance and permission to reproduce their photo graphs. The Macmillan Co. have kindly given permission for the quotations of Franklin, from Smyth, *The Writings of Benjamin Franklin*, the University of Chicago Press for the quotation from Millikan, *Electrons (+ and −), Protons, Photons, Neutrons, and Cosmic Rays*, and the editors of *Nature* for the quotations from their journal. Finally, I want to express my appreciation for the kind forbearance and helpful assistance of the Harvard University Press.

A. K. S.

Cambridge, Massachusetts
January–February, 1940

CONTENTS

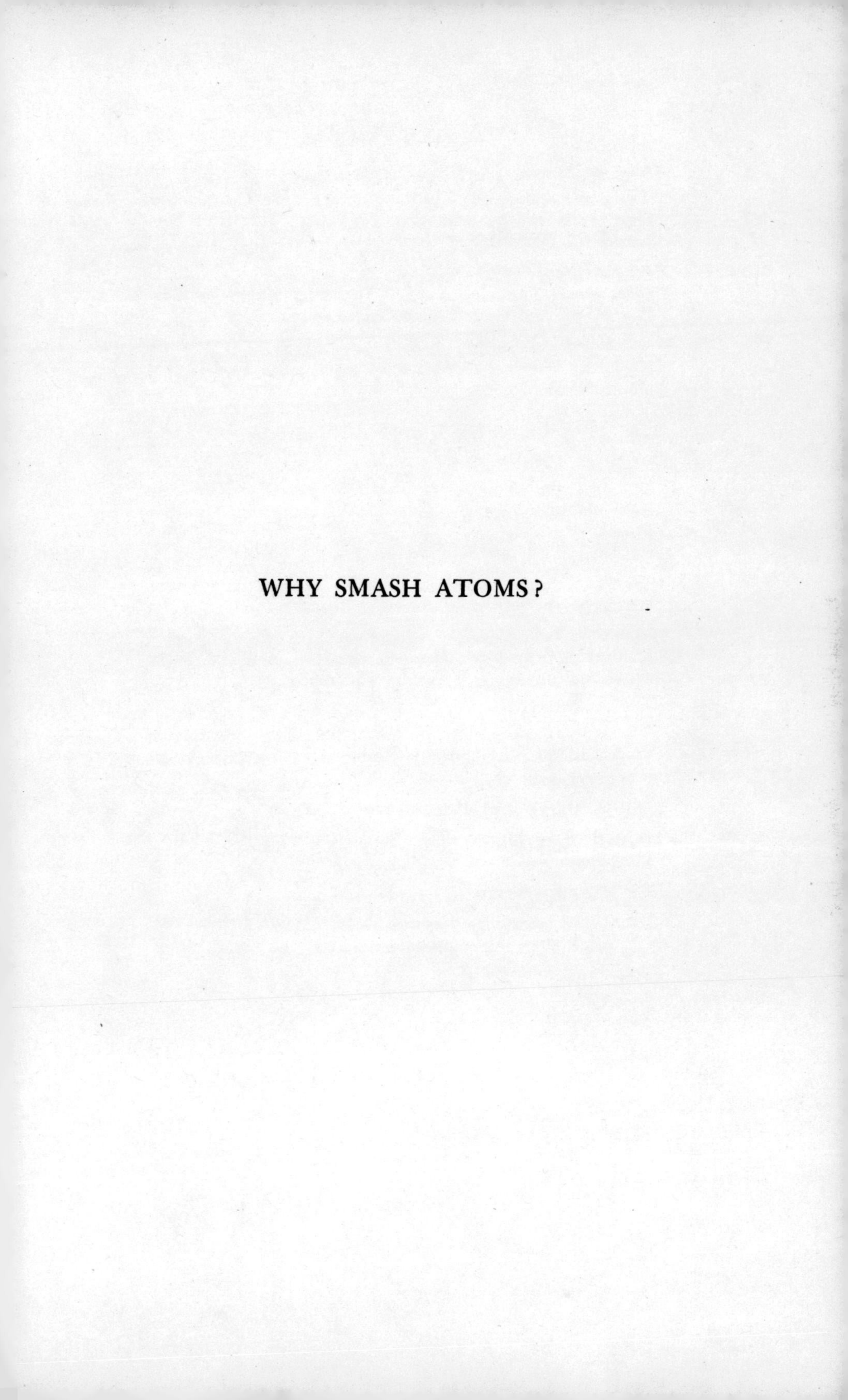

WHY SMASH ATOMS?

INTRODUCTION

THE atomic bomb is a technological development of the highest political significance. Nonetheless, important as it is, it is not the answer to the question in the title; it is a by-product of our attempts to learn the laws of nature. This by-product is not the first, nor will it be the last, to emerge as a result of untrammeled scientific research.

Modern nuclear physics may be said to have sprung from the triple scientific discoveries that illumined the years 1895 to 1897. In 1895 Röntgen discovered the x-ray; in 1896 Becquerel discovered radioactivity; in 1897 Thomson identified the electron. The work that began in these European countries has been extended and carried on all over the world. A necessary prerequisite for an appreciation of modern advances is a knowledge of this early work, as well as an understanding of the machines of modern physics. Research, sometimes patient, sometimes inspired, has led us to new knowledge and brought us to manifold new frontiers, until we now stand on the threshold of atomic power.

This history has been punctuated with by-product discoveries that have contributed tremendously to the welfare of the human race. From x-rays have come the modern machines which now make possible mass x-ray therapy for the prevention of tuberculosis on the one hand, and inspection of giant castings to insure the safety of modern machines on the other. Radioactivity has brought us an alleviation of cancer, and provided a notable tool for the investigation of all biological phenomena. The ubiquitous electron has been put to work in all manner of devices, from electric heaters to radar, and today the technology of electronics plays an important part in innumerable devices which we accept as modern necessities.

From these beginnings followed the manifold investigations into the atomic nucleus which led up, in 1939, to the discovery, almost simultaneously in Denmark, France, and the United States, of uranium fission. A further investigation of this phenomenon, the scientific inheritance of all the countries of the world, has led the United States to the development of the atomic bomb. There is no more reason now, than there was in 1919 when Rutherford first transmuted matter, to believe that the contemporary discovery is the pinnacle of scientific achievement.

The political significance of the atomic bomb is of infinite importance to us all. It has raised problems of tremendous social, economic, and political import. It is clear that our existence as a peaceful nation depends on a proper solution of these problems. World-wide agreement, peaceably reached in the real desire to control this new weapon for the benefit of all, will alone provide an opportunity for us to live free from the threat of war.

Only after such a solution to world affairs is reached, or at least only when such a solution is undertaken with an earnest desire of all the participants for success, can we speak of the scientific future. It will be seen that the atomic bomb has grown in this country by building upon our scientific inheritance from all over the world. There is no guarantee that these same problems will not be solved by scientists of other nations; in fact, in showing to the world so dramatically that the problem was soluble, we have materially assisted anyone who desires to repeat these experiments. Our achievement has placed us at the mercy of the world. There is nothing we can do to alter what we have made. We must realize the political implication of this new weapon and make aggressive use of our temporary scientific advantage to see that adequate world controls are carried out to safeguard freedom.

Untold further scientific advances still lie ahead. If we are to share in the advantages that will accrue from these new discoveries, we must ourselves make great contributions. For this, freedom of research is the only key. There is reason to fear that the purely scientific results of the atomic bomb project will not be published, although they are separable from the technology of the bomb itself. This is a desperate danger, indeed. Research is now a national matter. It we try to safeguard ourselves from the consequences of the atomic bomb, by repressing scientific fact, we will have taken a dreadful step. Repression can be no solution. To the four freedoms for which we have fought must be added a fifth, freedom of research.

PART I
WHAT IS AN ATOM?

CHAPTER 1

THE ELECTRON

BENJAMIN FRANKLIN was astute. His sagacity and keenness of discernment are evident in many of the observations he made about the nature of "electrical fire." The most famous Franklin electrical experiment, the use of a kite to catch electricity from a thunder-cloud, was not undertaken until 1752; by then he had established a considerable scientific reputation. Even in those days the calling of a physicist was not without its dangers; Professor Richmann was killed in St. Petersburg in 1753 while repeating the kite experiment. Franklin himself received several electrical shocks, one especially intense in his experiments on electrocuting fowl. These fowl he killed by the discharge of several Leyden jars connected together; describing the experiment, he wrote, "As six jars, however, discharged at once are capable of giving a very violent shock, the operator must be very circumspect lest he should happen to make the experiment on his own flesh, instead of that of the fowl."

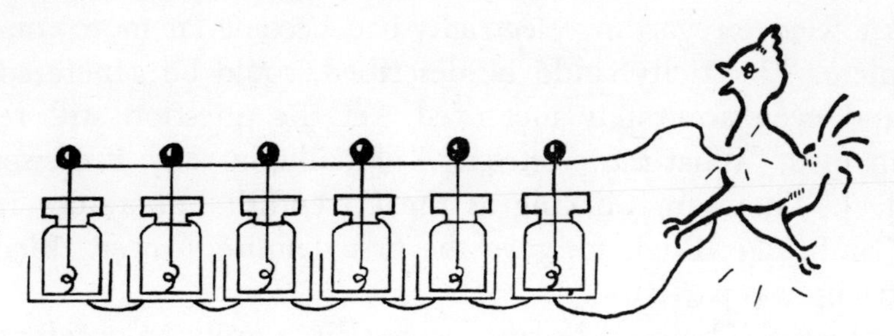

Generating electricity in the most primitive fashion, by the friction of a piece of silk rubbed over a glass rod, Franklin was able to carry out some very important experiments. He defined positive and negative electricity according to a convention which is still in force. He was aware of the fundamental and well known law which states that particles with opposite charges attract and particles with like charges repel one another, and he described an experiment which illustrated this law, "When a body is electrised *plus,* it will repel a positively electrified feather or small cork ball. When *minus,* . . . it will attract them. . . ."

It was natural to expect that a man of Franklin's inquisitive turn of mind would devise an explanation of the phenomena he observed. Accordingly he suggested that electricity was a fluid: positively charged matter contained an excess of the fluid, negatively charged matter lacked it. Thus began a century and a half of controversy. while scientific discussion raged on the nature of electricity. It was not a fruitless interval because many of the laws describing electricity were then first adequately formulated. Nonetheless, scientists were unable to decide just what electricity was. One school held Franklin's theory of the single fluid, another school, more numerous by far, believed that there were two fluids, one positive and one negative. There were even some who felt that electricity might be corpuscular, a theory supported by some interesting experimental evidence. By the end of the nineteenth century the body of knowledge regarding electricity had become far more complete. Electricity could be described, could be generated, and even accurately measured, yet the question still remained, "What *was* electricity?" Finally, in 1897, Professor J. J. Thomson, working at the Cavendish Laboratory in Cambridge, England, gave the first definite answer. Electricity was particles.

Joseph Thomson became a physicist purely by accident. Destined for an apprenticeship to a firm of locomotive makers, he learned that he would have to wait for a vacancy before beginning his apprenticeship. To pass the intervening time, he went to a small college in Manchester, his home town, and was there advised to try for a scholarship at Cambridge University. Thomson failed in his first examination, but, successful in obtaining a minor scholarship the next year, he entered Cambridge in 1876. Eight years later, when only twenty-eight, he succeeded Lord Rayleigh as Cavendish Professor — it was remarked that things had come to a pretty pass when mere boys were made professors. At Cambridge, Sir Isaac Newton had carried out his experiments in his own rooms; the Cavendish Laboratory was not opened until 1874. The Duke of Devonshire, then Chancellor of the University, founded the laboratory and the professorship which bear his family name of Cavendish. The first in its line of great professors was Clerk Maxwell, famous for his mathematical research on electricity. At his death, he was succeeded by Lord Rayleigh; then Thomson's brilliant researches carried on the Cavendish tradition. Knighted in 1908, Sir J. J. Thomson retired from the Cavendish Professorship in 1919; he then became master of Trinity College in Cambridge, the same college at which he had failed to obtain a scholarship in 1875. He died in December, 1940.

Thomson's suggestion that electricity consisted of particles was not new. During the century of controversy it had been put forward time and again. Thomson's work was important because, in his experiments on the conduction of electricity through gases, he proved that electricity was composed of discrete particles. By 1897 cathode rays had been discovered. These rays, produced in an evacuated tube by the application of a high voltage, were shot off at right angles from the face of the negative electrode sealed in the tube, the cathode. The position of the other electrode, the positive anode, a similar piece of metal sealed into the tube, did not affect the direction of the rays. They were always projected at right angles to the cathode. In France, Jean Perrin had shown that when these rays entered an insulated cylinder within the bulb they brought a negative charge to the cylinder. When he deflected the rays with a magnet — placing a magnet near the tube altered the path of the rays so they no longer entered the cylinder — the cylinder received no further negative charge. This experiment indicated that something electrified was given off from the cathode. But Thomson himself voiced the objections raised,

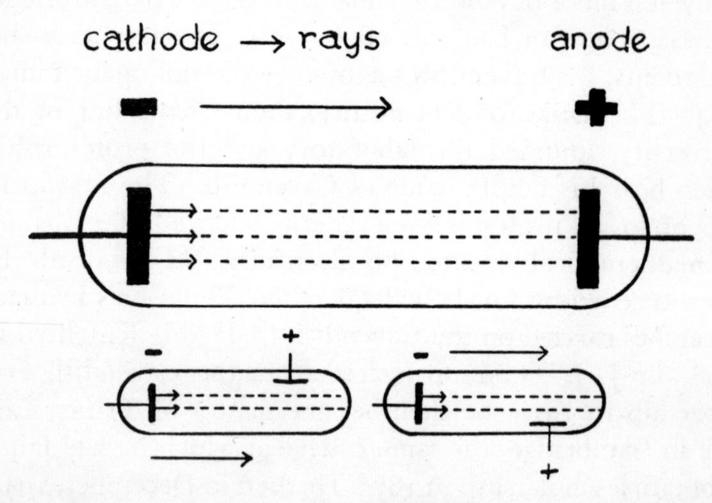

"Now the supporters of the aetherial theory do not deny that electrified particles are shot off from the cathode; they deny, however, that these charged particles have any more to do with the cathode rays than a rifle ball has with the flash when a rifle is fired."

Thereupon Thomson devised an experiment to prove unquestionably that the cathode rays were discrete negatively charged particles. At the extreme end of a long-necked glass flask he placed the cathode. The rays from the cathode, defined by passage through a pair of diaphragms, produced a bright spot of fluorescence on the end of the evacuated bulb. Just where the neck of the tube flared out into the bulb, Thomson placed a pair of parallel electrodes, which he used to deflect the beam electrically as it passed between them. Outside the tube he made use of an electro-

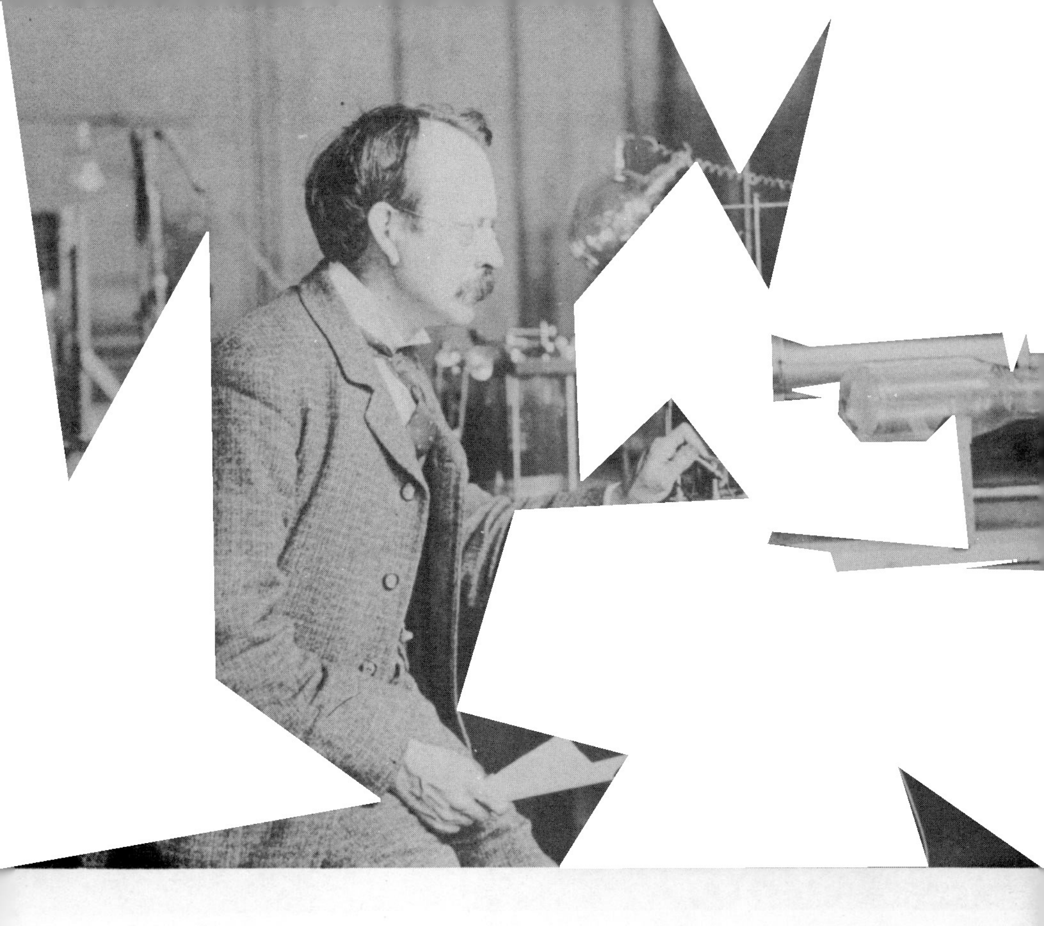

Professor J. J. Thomson about 1898.

In 1938, long after retiring from the Cavendish professorship, Sir J. J. Thomson is seated in the courtyard of the Cavendish laboratory, talking to the present professor, Sir William Bragg, left, waiting for the annual laboratory photograph.

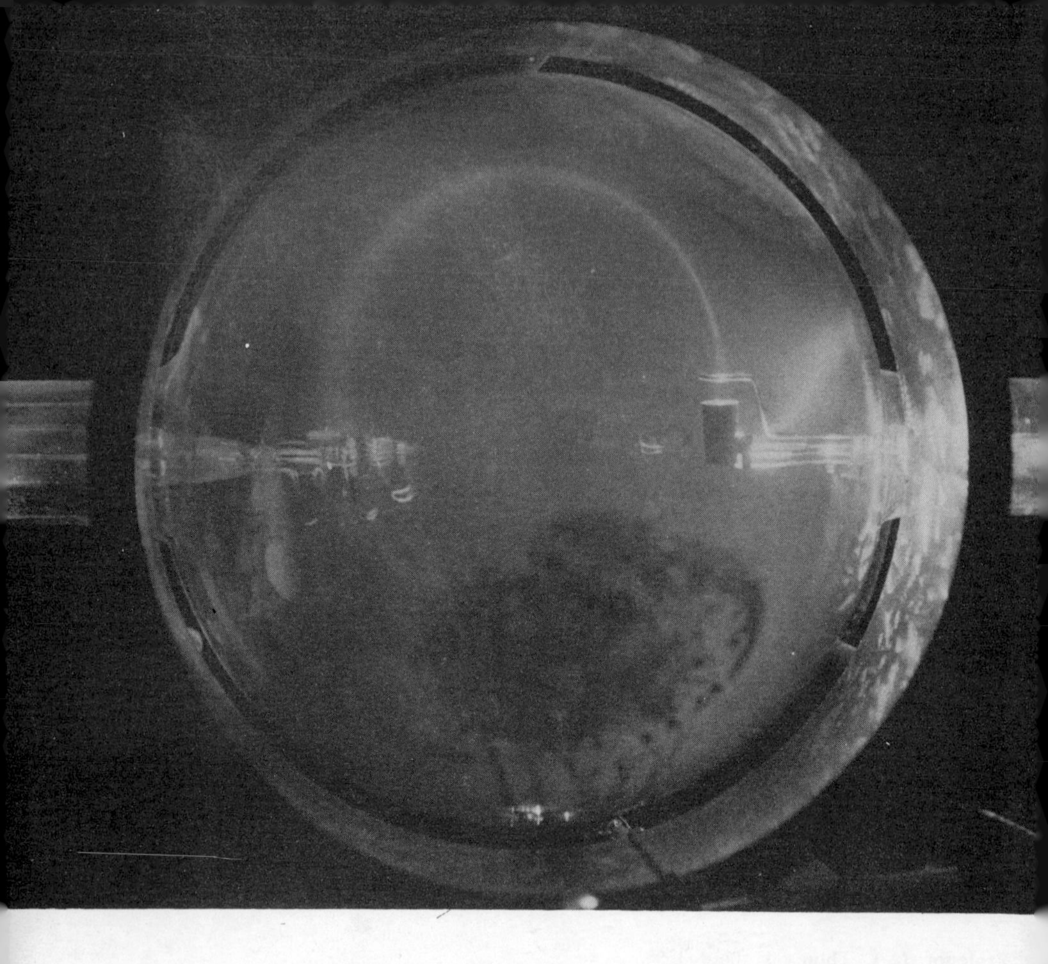

Deflection of an electron beam in a cathode ray tube. The beam can be seen deflecting between the two black plates at the right center.

Deflection of an electron beam in a magnetic field. The field is perpendicular to the plane of the paper. The electrons are shot out of the gun at the right of the picture and are curved in a circular track in the uniform magnetic field. In Thomson's experiment the beam was not deflected magnetically to so great an extent.

magnet, placed at right angles to the deflecting electrodes. Application of voltage to these electrodes caused the fluorescent spot produced by the beam to move from its central position on the bulb. Now, using the electromagnet — care-

Thomson — undeflected cathode rays

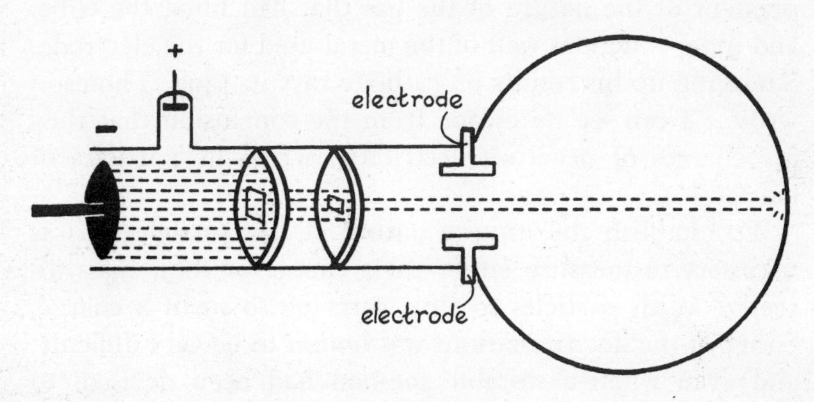

electrically deflected

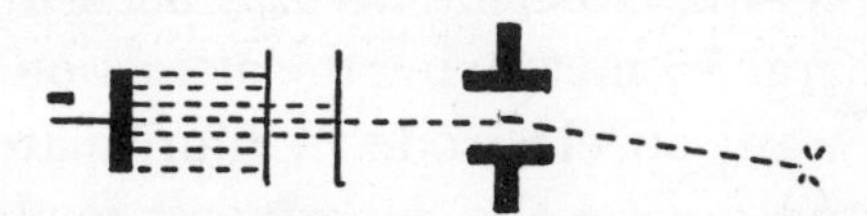

fully balancing the current through it with the voltage on the electrodes — Thomson was able to restore the spot

magnetically restored

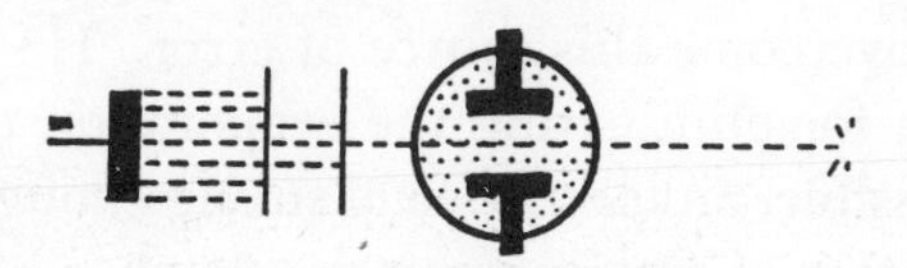

exactly to its undeflected position. From the values of the voltage and the current and the observed arrangement of plates and electromagnet, he could calculate at once the velocity of the particles causing the spot.

But the velocity was not information enough. It remained

to know the mass and the charge of the particles, now called electrons. Thomson's experiment could not provide these two values independently; however, from a knowledge of the deflection caused by the magnet alone, he could calculate their ratio. Further experiments showed that the ratio of the charge to the mass of the particles was a constant independent of the nature of the gas that had filled the tube, and independent as well of the metal used for the electrode. Summing up his results on cathode rays in 1897, Thomson wrote, "I can see no escape from the conclusion that they are charges of negative electricity carried by particles of matter."

To establish the unique nature of the particles it was necessary to measure either their charge or their mass directly. With particles so tiny, carrying so small a charge, either of the determinations was bound to be very difficult; and even when a suitable method had been devised, to require painstaking and accurate work. Under Professor Thomson's direction, experiments had been undertaken to estimate the charge by measuring the attraction of a charged water cloud toward an electrode. Unfortunately, evaporation of the cloud during the experiment made the results inaccurate.

In 1909, Robert Millikan at the University of Chicago, now a Nobel laureate and director of the physics laboratory at California Institute of Technology, began experiments designed to overcome this source of error. He wrote, "My original plan for eliminating the evaporation error was to obtain, if possible, an electric field strong enough exactly to balance the force of gravity upon the cloud. . . . It was not found possible to balance the cloud, as had been originally planned, but it was found possible to do something much better: namely, to hold the individual charged drops suspended by the field for periods varying from 30 to 60 seconds." To make the drop visible, the space between the electrodes was brightly illuminated and the drop itself observed through a small telescope. Millikan says, "These drops appear as perfectly distinct bright points. I have on several occasions obtained but one single such 'star' in the whole field and held it there for nearly a minute."

But the water drops also evaporated, so Millikan was forced to use oil drops to eliminate the error completely. The chamber in which the movement of the drops was observed consisted of two parallel electrodes set a short distance apart, carefully shielded against any stray currents of air. The droplets, sprayed from a common atomizer, formed a mist in a compartment above the top plate. Some of them, already charged by friction during ejection from the atomizer, entered the observation chamber below through a tiny hole in the plate. Here they could be observed through a telescope either falling under gravity, or rising, when the voltage applied to the electrodes was great enough to overcome gravity. Millikan sometimes observed that the droplets, rising in the electric field — application of voltage to the electrodes produces an electric field between them —

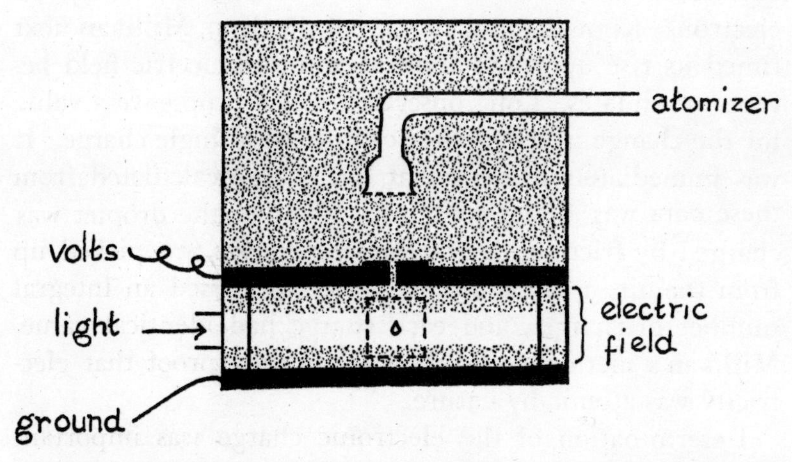

suddenly changed their velocity. This change he ascribed to capture of a charge from, or loss to, the air which surrounded the droplet; and he identified the charges as electrons.

To find the size of the drops, Millikan timed the rate of their free fall under gravity. The experiment was so painstaking, and the results so exact, that a new check had to be made on the laws relating to such fall, and a new determination made of the viscosity of the air. He found at once that the weight of the electron was negligible compared even to the weight of so tiny a droplet. The rate of fall remained constant whether the oil drop carried one or twenty-two electrons. Knowing now the size of the drop, Millikan next timed its rise upon the application of an electric field between the plates. Long observation of a drop gave a value for the change in speed after capture of a single charge. It was immediately evident that the charge calculated from these data was always constant. Whether the droplet was charged by friction, or whether the charge was picked up from the air, a given droplet always possessed an integral number of charges, and each charge had identical value. Millikan's meticulous work was the final proof that electricity was atomic by nature.

Determination of the electronic charge was important because it signified increased physical knowledge. In physics the tiny charge on an electron is a fundamental constant: it is the irreducible element of charge associated with the smallest known mass. The mass in grams is so small that it requires 27 ciphers after the decimal point before the first significant figure; the charge in coulombs requires 18 ciphers. All charge, positive and negative, is atomic, and the absolute value of the charge of the electron gives the size of the indivisible electrical unit.

In practical life electrons are also of great importance. Nowhere is their action more apparent than in radio and television. The picture painted on the end of a television tube is painted there by an electron beam. The movement of the beam, as it sweeps up and down, over and across the

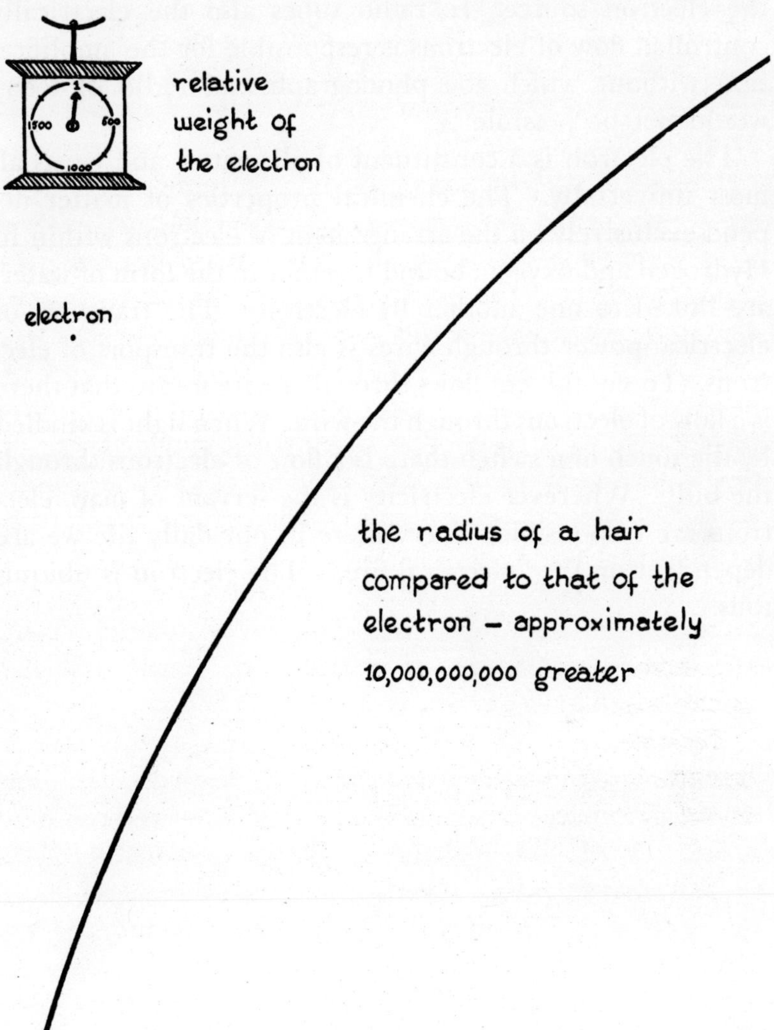

screen, is controlled by electric fields, exactly like the beam in Thomson's early tube. The sole difference is that the electrons are given off by a hot filament, a small wire coil heated by electricity like the coils in an automobile cigarette lighter. Since a hot filament in a vacuum will give off electrons much more readily than a cold one, television tubes, as well as radio tubes, use hot filaments to provide the electron source. In radio tubes also the electrically controlled flow of electrons is responsible for the amplification without which the phonograph and radio of today would not be possible.

The electron is a constituent of all matter and exists almost universally. The chemical properties of matter depend exclusively on the arrangement of electrons within it. Hydrogen and oxygen, bound together in the form of water, are linked to one another by electrons. The transport of electrical power through wires is also the transport of electrons. To say current flows through a wire means that there is a flow of electrons through the wire. When light is kindled by the touch of a switch there is a flow of electrons through the bulb. Wherever electricity is the servant of man, electrons are responsible. Everywhere in our daily life we are dependent on the "electrical fire." The electron is ubiquitous.

CHAPTER 2

THE PROTON

LIKE Topsy, the proton just grew. Nobody ever discovered it; recognition of its fundamental importance grew slowly from 1886 until 1920 when the proton finally received its name. In 1886, Goldstein, a German scientist in Berlin, observed a phenomenon previously unnoticed in studies on the conduction of electricity through gases. To investigate the phenomenon he constructed a cathode of metal netting and placed it in the exact center of a discharge tube. With this tube he could observe not only the electrons issuing

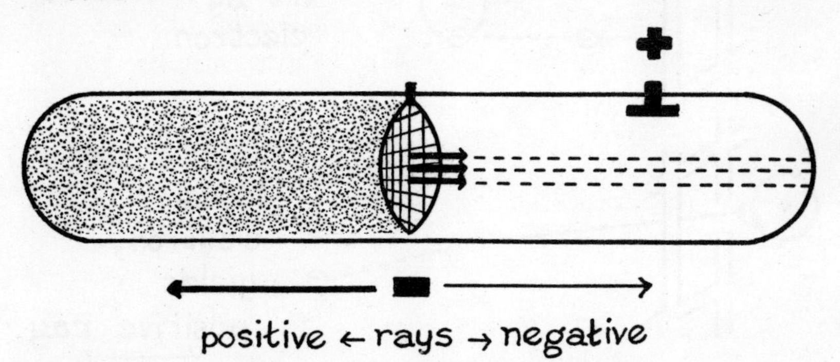

from the cathode in a forward direction, but also the newly discovered radiation behind it. Describing his results to the German Royal Academy, Goldstein wrote, "I was then . . . very much surprised to see the cathode surrounded with a pale golden yellow light, which, penetrating the net, filled up the whole space from the cathode to the wall completely."

The pale golden yellow radiation is now known to be a positive radiation, very different from the electrons produced so prolifically in the electric discharge. The electrons issue from the cathode in the forward direction, that is in the region between the negative electrode and the positive one. On this side of the cathode an electric field exists: it is one of the peculiarities of such discharge tubes that the field

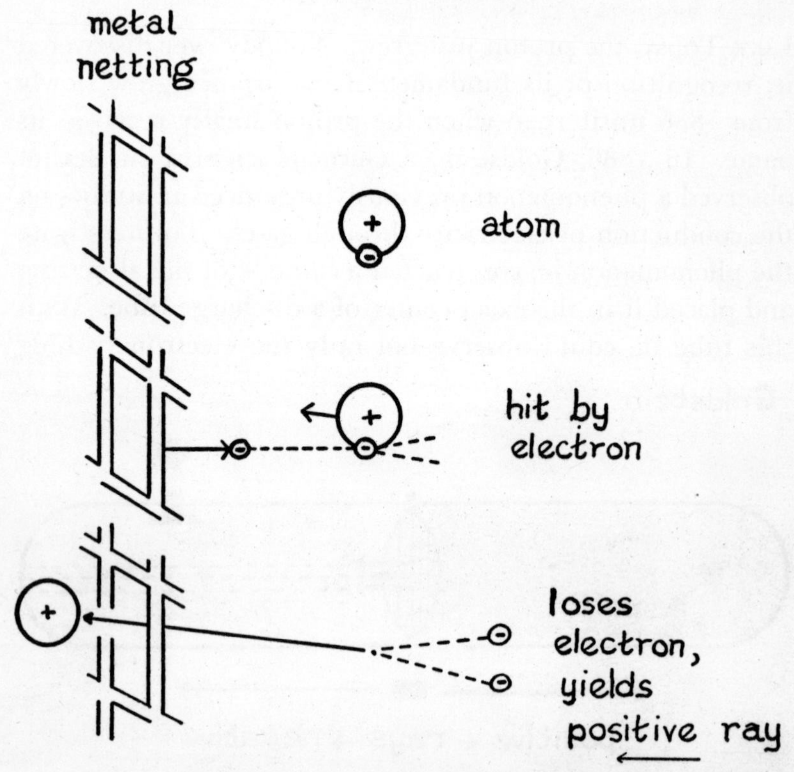

is only very strong directly in front of the cathode. Consequently, the electrons always issue from the cathode in a forward direction, regardless of the actual position of the anode. With the field concentrated in the region immediately in front of the cathode, the electrons receive their full energy at the beginning of their path, and, once past the intense region, continue to coast in the same direction they took initially.

The atom is electrically neutral, containing both positive

and negative particles. The negative particles, electrons, are bound far more loosely in the atomic structure than the positive ones. The electrons produced in a discharge are able to knock these very light, loosely bound electrons out of the atom, leaving behind a heavy positively charged kernel. It is this kernel, charged because it has lost one or more electrons, that is responsible for the radiation noted by Goldstein. The kernel of the hydrogen atom, that is the hydrogen atom minus one electron, is called the proton. The proton possesses a single positive charge, equal and opposite to the charge on the electron. Its mass, however, is far greater than that of the electron; the proton weight is equal to that of 1840 electrons.

Some positively charged atoms are produced by electrons in the region of the intense field, and bearing a positive charge, are accelerated towards the negative electrode. The positive rays which impinge on a solid electrode are immediately lost. However, if the cathode is made of metal

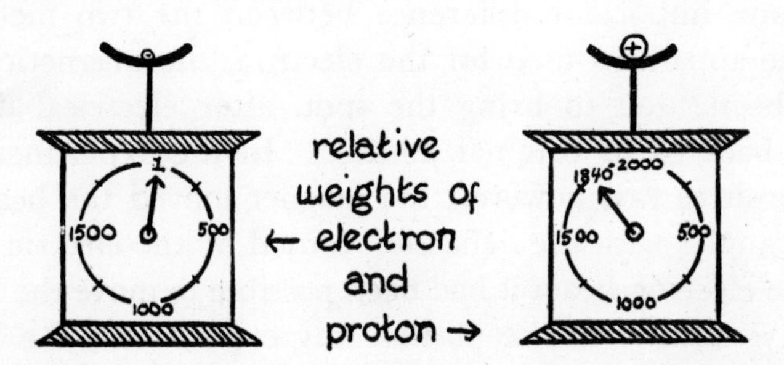

netting, some of the positive rays can go through the holes and continue their path in the field-free space beyond the electrode. The positive rays, produced immediately in front of the electrode, are characteristic of the very low pressure gas inside the tube. Goldstein described them thus: "The color of these rays, that we have so far described as 'gold,' varies with the nature of the gas in which the cathode finds itself. The rays are golden yellow in pure nitrogen . . . ; in hydrogen their color is rose, yellow-rose in oxygen, and a greenish grey-white in carbon dioxide."

In the hands of J. J. Thomson, further experiments on the positive radiation led to a determination of the mass of the positive particles. Goldstein was unable to deflect these heavy particles magnetically: because of their great weight, deflection of the positive rays requires a very intense magnetic force. In 1898, another scientist succeeded in bending the beam of particles as it passed through the magnetic field formed between the poles of a strong electromagnet. Then, in 1910, J. J. Thomson built a tube in which he applied the same principles that had yielded such important results in his earlier work on the electron. In his apparatus, a beam of particles penetrated a small channel drilled through the cathode, passed through both an electric and a magnetic field, and finally struck a fluorescent screen. The positive particle, like the electron, produces a star-like scintillation when it falls on such a screen. There was one important difference between the two methods. In the apparatus used for the electron, the magnetic field had been used to bring the spot, after electrical deflection, back to its original position. In the experiment on the positive ray, however, the magnet moved the beam at right angles with the deflection caused by the electric field. In the electron beam it had been possible to move the beam only vertically; in the positive ray experiment, the beam was deflected vertically by the electric field, and horizontally by the magnetic field. With such an apparatus Thomson found that all particles with the same ratio of mass to charge fell on his fluorescent screen on one smooth curve, a parabola, independent of the velocity with which the particles were traveling. The difference in velocity caused the particles to fall on different portions of the parabola, but the position of the parabola on the screen was determined solely by the ratio of mass to charge of the particles.

Production of a beam of positive particles was itself very difficult. To produce enough particles to register on a fluorescent screen, or a photographic plate, it was necessary to use a large flask, the entrance of which was closed by the cathode. The pressure in the flask was higher than that in the rest of the apparatus; the particles produced in the flask

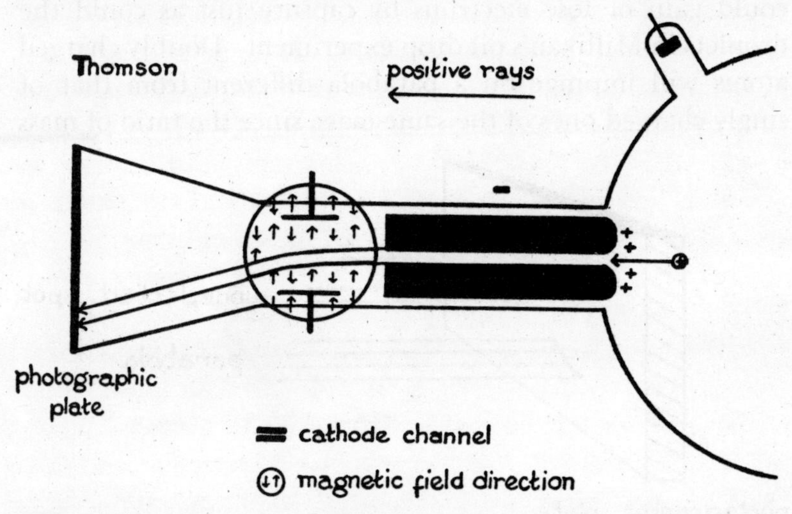

passed through a tiny channel drilled in the center of the cathode on into the deflecting fields beyond. The anode was sealed into the large flask off at one side. Great care was required in drilling the channel through the cathode; it had to be absolutely straight, and so tiny that it was almost impossible to see through it. Further, it had to be long enough for the particles to emerge as a well defined beam. The particles themselves often hit the side of the channel and ate it like a sand-blast, causing the channel to silt up; its limited life considerably increased the experimental difficulties. The beam issued from the channel into a tube which was large enough to accommodate the electrodes, and was flared out at the end for the fluorescent screen. Even here the troubles of the beam were not over. For one thing, the pressure in the deflecting section had to be much lower than that in the bulb, otherwise the beam would disperse by collision with other particles. With so small a channel the air could be pumped out of the camera side, even while the pressure required for discharge was maintained in the large flask. But a low pressure did not completely free the beam from interference. The positively charged particles could gain or lose electrons by capture just as could the droplets in Millikan's oil drop experiment. Doubly charged atoms will impinge on a parabola different from that of singly charged ones of the same mass, since the ratio of mass

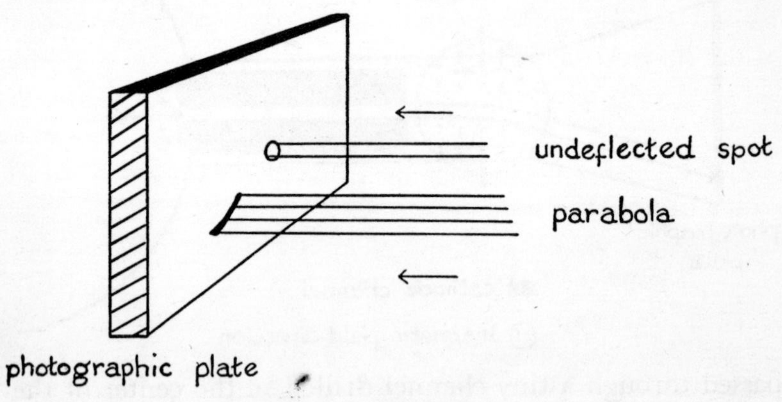

to charge of the doubly charged atoms is just half that of the single ones. Measurement of the position of the parabola relative to the undeflected spot gave a value for the mass of the particles. The charge was the electronic charge or some small multiple of it, since positive and negative charges have exactly the same numerical value. The ratio of mass to charge measured from the photographic plate provided a direct determination of the mass. Thomson's positive ray parabolas gave the first physical measurement of the masses of heavy particles.

By 1910 chemical measurement of the weights of the atoms had reached high accuracy. But chemical measurements differed greatly from the physical measurements of Thomson. Chemical weights are always compared with oxygen — a standard to which a weight of 16 has been arbitrarily assigned. Work with chemical compounds means work with vast quantities of atoms, since the number of atoms in a weighable amount of matter is astronomically large. Consequently the weight determined by chemical means is an average weight. If a given element were composed of two kinds of particles, each differing slightly in weight, chemical analysis would not reveal the difference; the measured weight would be the average of the two. On the other hand, Thomson's positive ray analysis would reveal the difference, for there would be two parabolas with different positions, each corresponding to the mass of one of the two constituent particles.

With neon, a gaseous element whose chemical weight is 20.2, Thomson found that he was absolutely unable to resolve his results into just one parabola no matter how carefully he purified the neon. Whenever he introduced neon into his apparatus, he always obtained two parabolas. Describing his results, he wrote: "There can, therefore, I think, be little doubt that what has been called neon is not a simple gas, but a mixture of two gases, one of which has an atomic weight of about 20, and the other about 22. The parabola due to the heavier gas is always much fainter than that due to the lighter, so probably the heavier gas forms only a small percentage of the mixture."

One striking result Thomson obtained was that the physical masses of the elements he measured were given by whole numbers compared with oxygen, to which the number 16 was arbitrarily assigned. Further development of the apparatus has led to an extension of these results. After the war, Aston, who had assisted in Thomson's experiments, developed apparatus for obtaining the masses of the elements much more precisely than was possible by Thomson's parabola method. In Aston's apparatus — he received the Nobel prize for its development — particles of the same mass converge at one spot on a photographic plate, regardless of the velocity with which they are propagated. This apparatus Aston christened the mass-spectrograph. When a beam of light is passed into an ordinary spectrograph, it is resolved into its component colors, and all the light of one color, say a particular shade of blue, comes to a focus on the same spot. In the mass-spectrograph the rays produced in a discharge

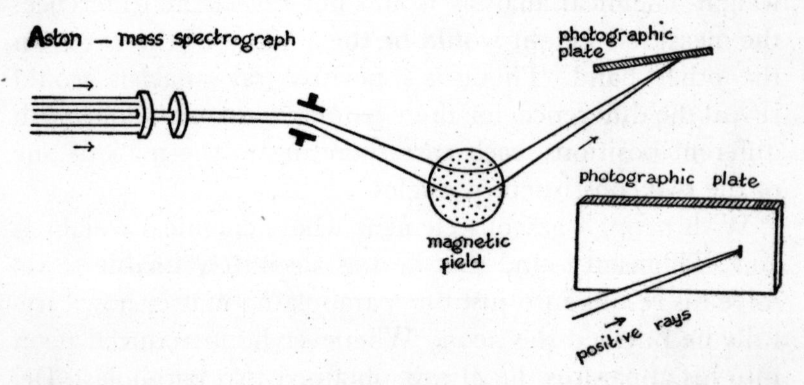

tube penetrate the cathode and emerge, after passage between two diaphragms, as a thin ribbon of positive rays. These rays are first deflected by an electric field, and then by a magnetic field; the intensity and shapes of these fields are arranged to compensate for any difference in velocity. Consequently, all the atoms of one mass strike the plate on a single short straight line. A single line is much more susceptible to exact measurement than a parabola, so Aston was able to obtain precise values of the physical masses of many of the elements. In America the apparatus has been still further modified, with far reaching improvements. In complete agreement with Thomson's early work, the masses of all the elements can be represented by whole numbers on the physical scale.

On this scale, the singly charged proton has a mass closely equal to unity, which suggests at once that the proton is the positive analogue of the electron. No positive ray of lighter

F. W. Aston, working with his mass spectrograph in the Cavendish laboratory.

Modern mass spectrograph – the equipment of K. T. Bainbridge at Harvard. The chamber which holds the photographic plate may be seen to the right and slightly above the magnet.

P. Donaldson

Associated Press

Sir James Chadwick.

Keystone-Underwood

Irène Curie-Joliot and her husband Frédéric Joliot.

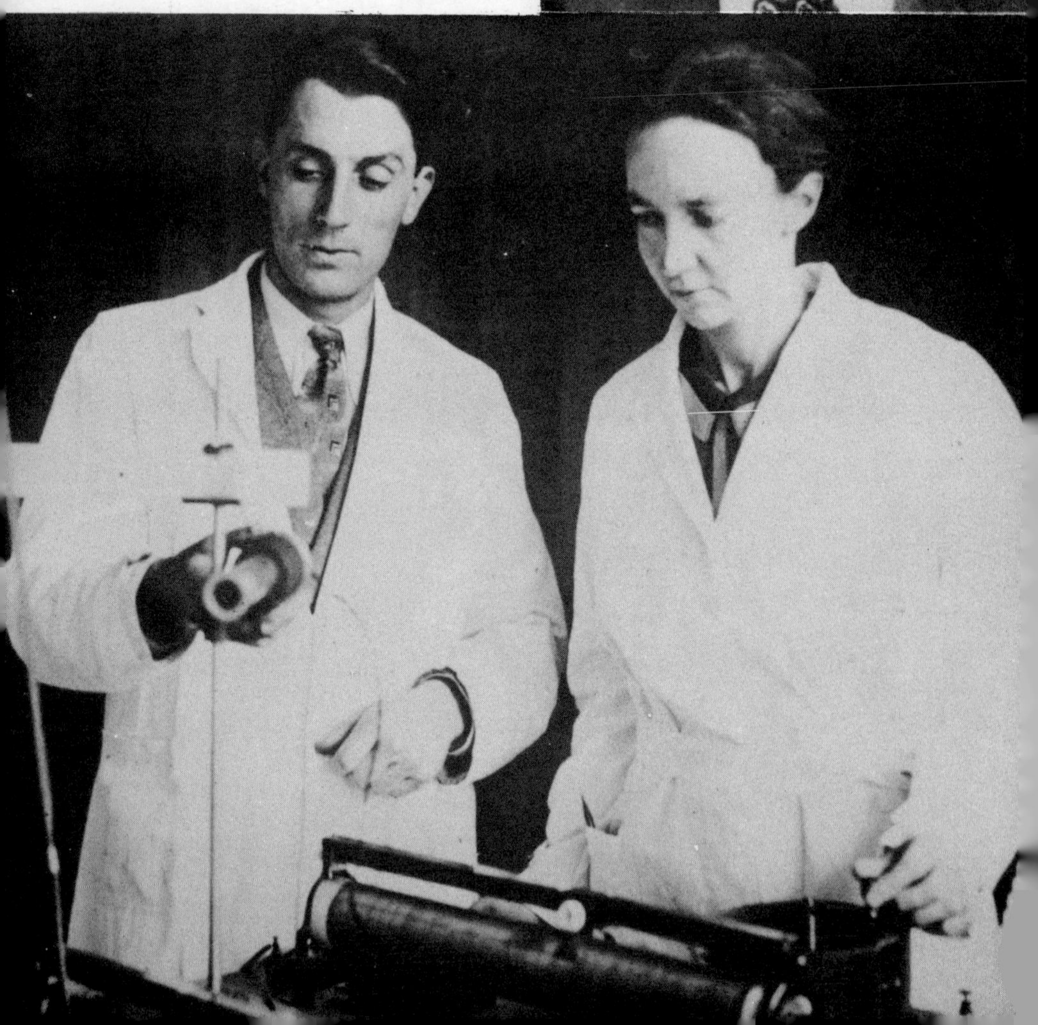

mass has ever been discovered in the mass-spectrograph, so in spite of the great disparity of mass, the proton was put forward as the fundamental positive particle. As early as 1815, William Prout, an English chemist, had proposed that hydrogen, whose chemical weight also is almost unity, was the common foundation element to all matter, and that all the other elements were composed from hydrogen. The information then available on chemical weights indicated that this could not be the case, so Prout's hypothesis was discarded.

But in 1920, Rutherford, who had succeeded Thomson as head of the Cavendish Laboratory, suggested the idea once again. Evidence that had accrued in Rutherford's brilliant researches as well as that provided by the mass-spectrograph indicated that the singly charged hydrogen atom was a fundamental particle. Rutherford made this proposal first in his famous Bakerian lecture before the Royal Society in 1920, and again in a paper presented before the British Association for the Advancement of Science that same year. In the discussion following, Sir Oliver Lodge suggested that the particle be named proton. The name seemed so satisfactory that it was soon adopted, though not without opposition. Indeed, a year or two afterwards it was suggested in all seriousness that the name be changed to Prouton, in Prout's honor. However, the singly charged hydrogen atom is still a proton.

CHAPTER 3

THE NEUTRON

THE neutron is a prediction that came true. In that same famous Bakerian lecture in 1920, Rutherford suggested the existence of a particle having the properties of a neutron. At that time the only particles known were charged, the electron with unit negative charge, and the heavy proton with unit positive charge. The neutron, as its name implies, was visualized as a particle with no charge; and with a mass almost equal to that of the proton. An uncharged particle

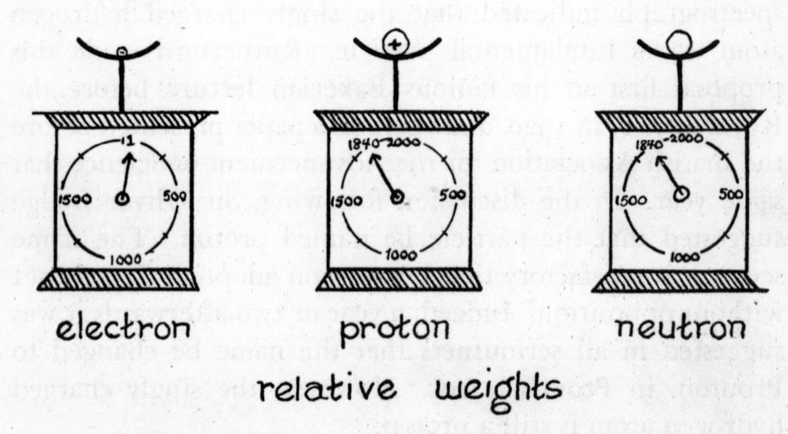

would behave far differently from a charged one; for example, having no charge it would be entirely unaffected by an electrical field. The neutron, indeed, would act like a ghost of a proton, gliding unnoticed through solid barriers. Rutherford himself said, "Such an atom would have very novel properties. . . . It should be able to move freely through matter . . . and it may be impossible to contain it in a sealed vessel."

So impressed was Rutherford with the possibilities of

this particle that he instituted a search for it at the Cavendish Laboratory. Reasoning that in an electrical discharge in a tube filled with hydrogen the components of his proposed particle, the proton and the electron, were both present in great quantities, he envisaged the possibility of producing neutrons by means of such a discharge. But the proton proved too highly armed to succumb to so feeble an attack. The experiments failed and the idea lay dormant for twelve years.

During these twelve years, experiments on the disintegration of the atom had come into prominence. When an atom disintegrates, it sometimes gives off a gamma ray, a non-corpuscular radiation of great penetrating power, similar to the x-ray. In 1930, two German scientists found evidence of a particularly penetrating gamma radiation given off from the light but tough metal, beryllium, when it was disintegrated by the rays from the natural radioactive element polonium. The new powerful gamma radiation had an energy more than five times greater than that of gamma rays from any known radioactive substance.

Then in Paris on the 18th of January in 1932, M. Joliot, and his wife Irene, daughter of Mme. Curie, presented their first report on the absorption of the new radiation in matter. The necessary apparatus was simple, consisting merely of a source, again beryllium excited by polonium radiation, and

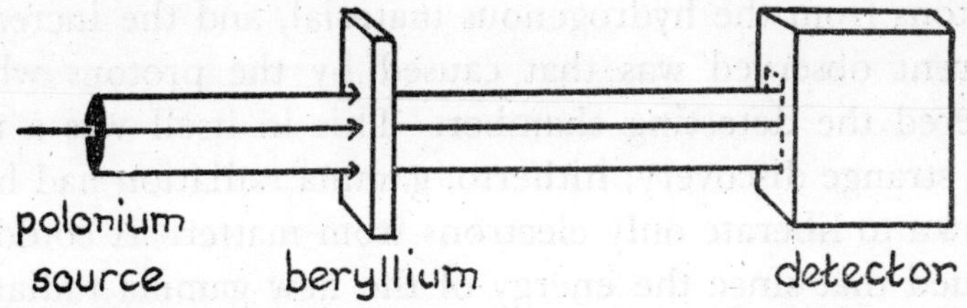

an electrical detector. With an unimpeded path between the beryllium and the detector, the radiation caused a flow of current in the detector. When, however, screens of any absorbing material were placed between the beryllium and the detector, less radiation was able to reach the detector, and the observed flow of current diminished. The absorption of the radiation in screens constructed from most elements did indeed lower the resulting current, but in some

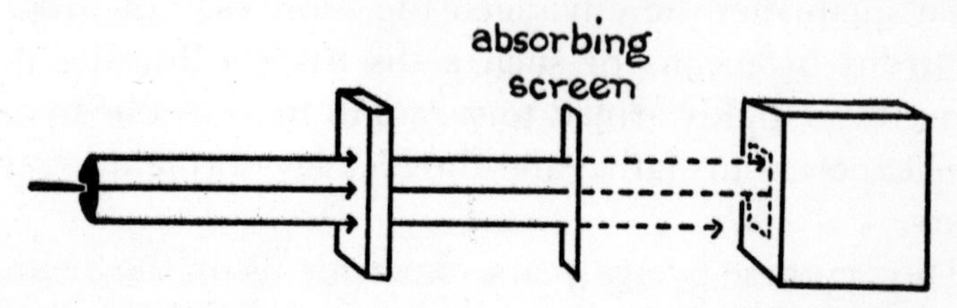

exceptional cases Mme. Curie-Joliot and M. Joliot observed: "On the contrary, the current increases notably when one interposes screens of substances containing hydrogen, like paraffin, water, and cellophane. The most intense effect has

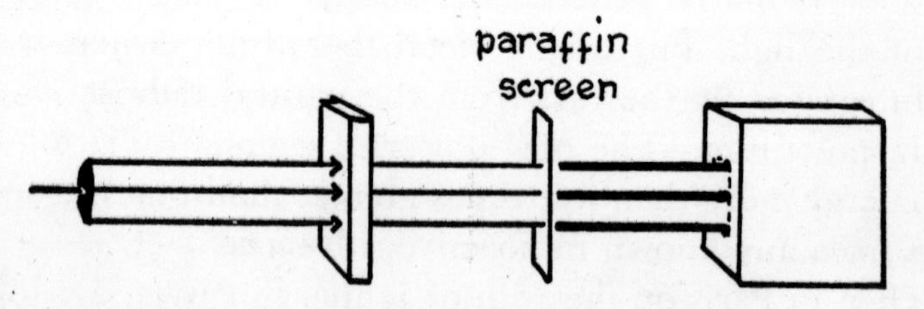

been observed with paraffin; the current increases almost by a factor of two in this case."

There was but one explanation which could account for this phenomenon. The radiation caused the ejection of protons from the hydrogenous material, and the increased current observed was that caused by the protons which entered the detecting chamber. This in itself was a new and strange discovery; hitherto, gamma radiation had been known to liberate only electrons from matter. It could be argued that since the energy of the new gamma radiation was far greater than any energies before observed, then the interaction of the radiation might be different from any interaction known before. This was the explanation that Curie and Joliot put forward.

Fascinated by these results, they carried their researches even further, and they soon found that the radiation was capable of projecting atoms heavier than protons. The interposition of thin screens containing heavier elements than hydrogen between the source and the detector also resulted in a slight current increase. If it had been difficult to explain the projection of protons before, now it was even more difficult to explain the projection of these heavier elements. In fact, the gamma radiation did not obey in any way the laws which had hitherto been applicable to such radiation. Summing up their work, on February 22, 1932, Curie and Joliot were able to report to the French Academy of Sciences that, "If one attempts to apply the formulas which permit the calculation of absorption . . . one arrives at results incompatible with the experimental facts. . . . It is possible to believe that the effect of the absorption of the penetrating gamma rays . . . corresponds to a new mode of interaction of radiation with matter."

Meanwhile, at the Cavendish Laboratory in England, James Chadwick, now Professor at Liverpool, inspired by the first work of Curie and Joliot, began research on the strange radiation. In a letter to the English periodical *Nature*, dated February 17, 1932, Chadwick wrote: "I have made some experiments. . . . The results I have obtained in the course of the work are very difficult to explain on the assumption that the radiation from beryllium is" gamma radiation, "if energy and momentum are to be conserved in the collisions." The principles of conservation of momentum and conservation of energy are two of the principles physics holds dearest: whenever some new discovery seems about to throw doubt on their validity, every effort is made to find some explanation which will retain these fundamental principles. Chadwick goes on: "The difficulties disappear, however, if it be assumed that the radiation consists of particles of mass 1 and charge 0, or neutrons. . . . It is to be expected that many of the effects of a neutron in passing through matter should resemble those of a [gamma ray] of high energy, and it is not easy to reach the final decision between the two hypotheses. Up to the present, all the evidence is in favor of the neutron, while the [gamma ray] hypothesis can only be upheld if the conservation of energy and momentum be relinquished at some point."

Following upon its discovery, the neutron was established as a fundamental particle. This newly accredited neutron was able to account for all the strange properties hitherto attributed to the radiation. The grave difficulties that so long delayed the discovery of the neutron resulted from its lack of charge. Curie and Joliot had attempted to deflect the radiation with a magnet, but they were unsuccessful, for the neutrons which have no charge can not be bent by a uniform magnetic field any more than can the supposed gamma rays which have no mass. With no charge there is no electrical handle to grasp the neutron by. Consequently it can penetrate the electrical barriers of other atoms to the massive core within.

On Chadwick's neutron hypothesis, it is easy to account for the projection of hydrogen from materials like paraffin. The mass of the neutron on the physical scale is 1.0090, just a little heavier than the proton with a mass of 1.0076. When a fast-moving neutron collides with a stationary particle of equal size, it gives up a large fraction of its energy to the particle. The struck particle moves off with energy acquired from the neutron, which itself continues with diminished speed. Thus one billiard ball projects another. However, after collision with a far heavier particle, the neutron usually bounces harmlessly off. Similarly, it would be very difficult to project a cannon ball by hitting it with a billiard ball. The neutron, on the average, will share its energy with a proton: with heavier particles the average neutron will give up less and less of its energy.

Consequently, it is easy for the neutron to project protons from material containing hydrogen, but increasingly difficult for it to project heavier particles.

The path of the neutron as it traverses matter is not straight. Like a bullet it can ricochet from atom to atom

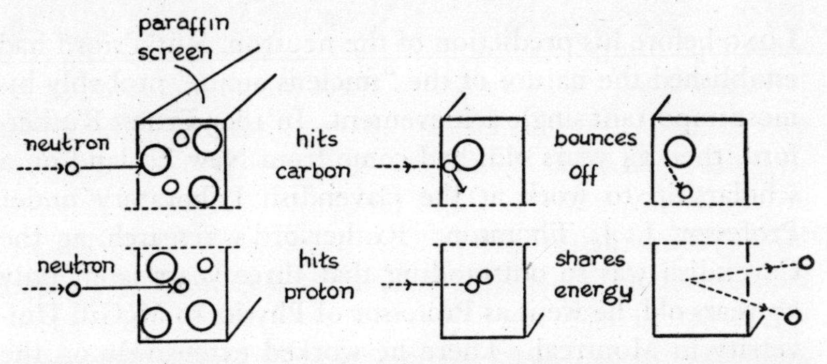

until its energy is spent. Collision with heavy atoms, like lead, does not use up any of the neutron energy, so a neutron can penetrate a thick lead wall with very little diminution of velocity. Since lead is useless, workers on modern atom smashers, prolific sources of neutrons, must protect themselves with walls of water. The three foot thick water tanks which are used are themselves not completely opaque to neutrons. Even in a water tank an exceptional neutron may travel back and forth for a distance of more than one hundred yards before it finally comes to rest. Lord Rutherford was right: it is impossible to contain the neutron in a sealed vessel.

CHAPTER 4

THE NUCLEUS ATOM

Long before his prediction of the neutron, Rutherford had established the nature of the "nucleus atom," probably his most important single achievement. In 1895 Ernest Rutherford, then 24 years old, had come from New Zealand on a scholarship to work at the Cavendish Laboratory under Professor J. J. Thomson. Rutherford's research at the Cavendish was so outstanding that three years later, only 27 years old, he went as Professor of Physics to McGill University in Montreal. There he worked extensively on the properties of radioactivity, so successfully that in 1908 he received the Nobel prize in chemistry. Speaking at a banquet in Stockholm before accepting the prize, he remarked that he had worked for a long time on transformations but he had witnessed none so quick as his own from physicist to chemist. In 1907, he had come back to England as Professor of Physics at Manchester, where he stayed until 1919, when he returned to Cambridge, succeeding Thomson as Cavendish Professor of Experimental Physics. Recognizing not only his outstanding scientific achievements, but also his noteworthy cooperation with the government in the promotion of research, George V created him baron in 1931. Rutherford chose as title, Lord Rutherford of Nelson; yet even after his baronetcy he preferred to be Professor rather than Lord Rutherford. In October, 1937, he died, aged but 66, and now lies buried in Westminster Abbey.

In 1896, not long after Rutherford had first come to England, Henri Becquerel in France discovered radioactivity — the spontaneous disintegration of elements, accompanied by emission of invisible rays. X-rays had been discovered only a few months previously, and at that time it was thought that the fluorescence that often accompanies x-radiation was in fact responsible for the production of x-rays. Fifteen years earlier Becquerel had prepared a uranium salt which he had found to fluoresce brilliantly. In order to test the theory he once again prepared the uranium salt and after wrapping it in black paper set the salt on a thin silver foil and then put them both on a photographic plate. As he had hoped, the photographic plate showed a darkening, indicating that the uranium salt did give off x-rays strong enough to penetrate the silver foil. On continuing his investigations, Becquerel soon found that the radiation he observed had no connection with fluorescence, or indeed with x-rays; that this radiation was a property of any mineral containing uranium. Becquerel had discovered radioactivity.

Just before he left for McGill, Rutherford began his research on the qualities of the radiation given off from uranium. He found that the radiations could be divided into two types, one intensely powerful but very short in range, which he called alpha radiation; and another less powerful, but faster and more penetrating, called beta radiation. Subsequent research has shown that both radiations are corpuscular. Alpha radiation is the very energetic expulsion of an alpha particle — a doubly charged helium atom — from the radioactive element, like a stone from a slingshot. Beta radiation is also a projection of particles, but the swift beta particles are the far lighter electrons. These particles are often accompanied by the emission of gamma rays, non-corpuscular radiation of great penetrating power, the same radiation which had been suggested to account for the results of the early neutron work.

After Becquerel's discovery, the work of the Curies and others, yielding as one result the discovery and isolation of radium, led also to the identification of many elements besides uranium which possessed the rare property of decomposing spontaneously with the emission of corpuscular radiation. In order to account for so many radioactive elements, Rutherford, working with Soddy, who also won a Nobel prize in chemistry, put forward the transformation theory, which states that a radioactive element after giving off an alpha or a beta particle has suffered a complete change

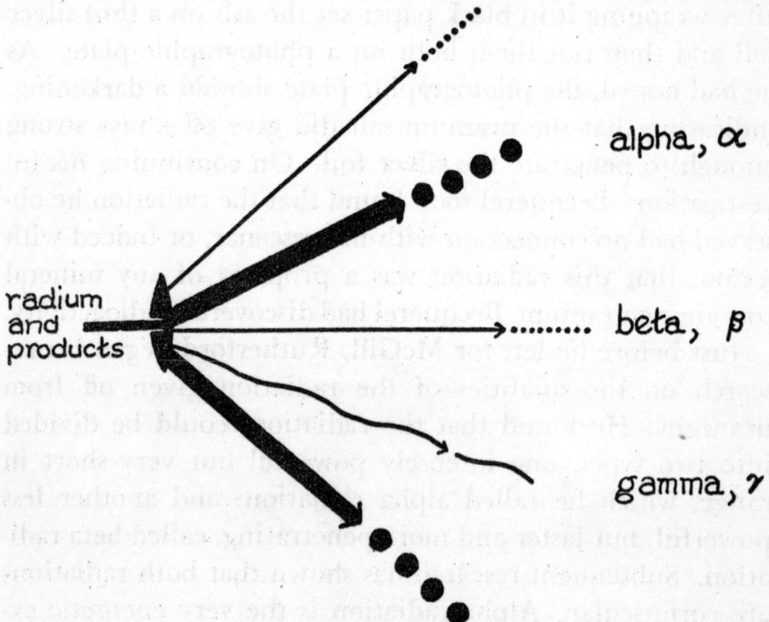

in its chemical nature and become an entirely different element. Following this theory it was found that all the radioactive elements could be classified neatly in three families, in each of which families the parent elements gave birth to daughter elements, and these daughters in turn gave birth to later descendants, all according to a perfectly defined genealogy.

At McGill in 1905, Rutherford found that a beam of alpha particles from a radioactive source was scattered in passing through thin films of aluminum. Similarly, an automobile headlight produces a clearly defined beam of light, but if the lens is covered with a thin handkerchief the beam

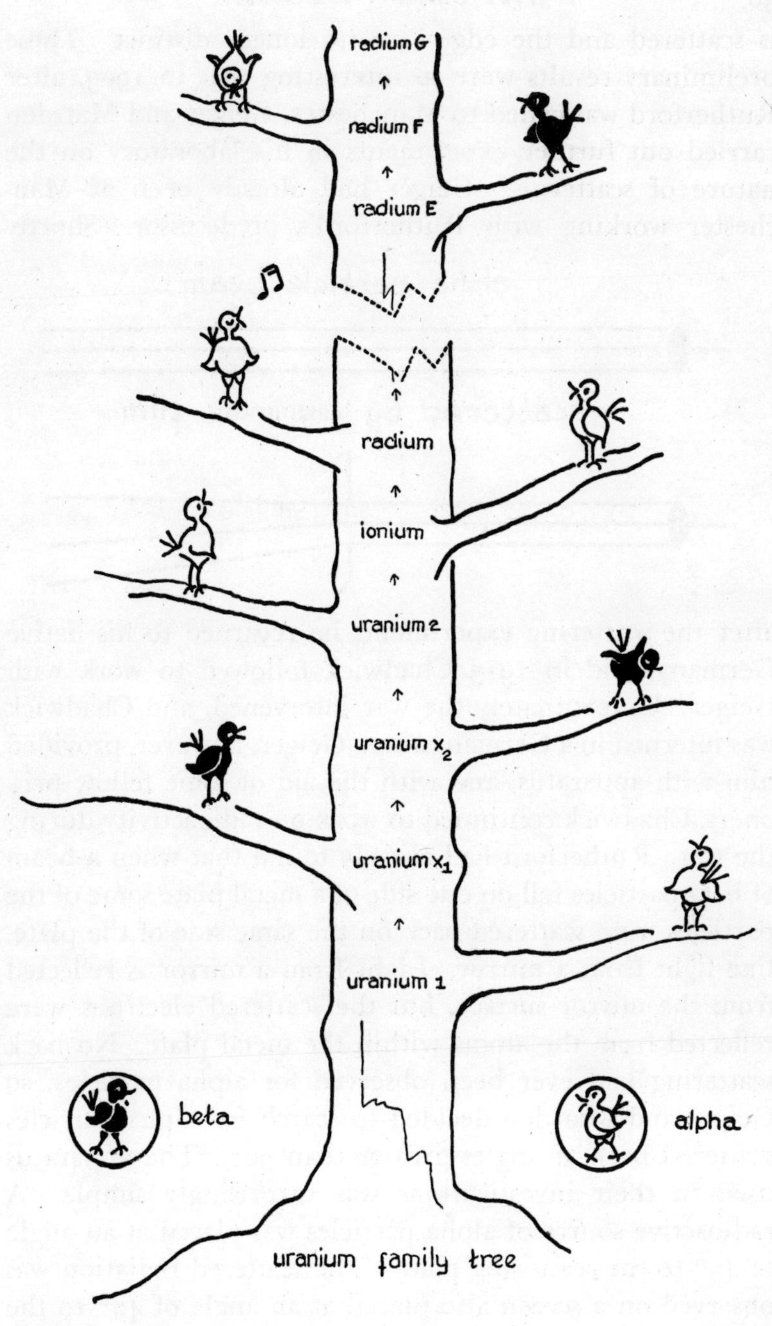

radium G
radium F
radium E
radium
ionium
uranium 2
uranium x_2
uranium x_1
uranium 1
beta
alpha
uranium family tree

is scattered and the edges are no longer distinct. These preliminary results were so interesting that in 1909, after Rutherford was called to Manchester, Geiger and Marsden carried out further experiments in his laboratory on the nature of scattering. Geiger had already been at Manchester working with Rutherford's predecessor. Shortly

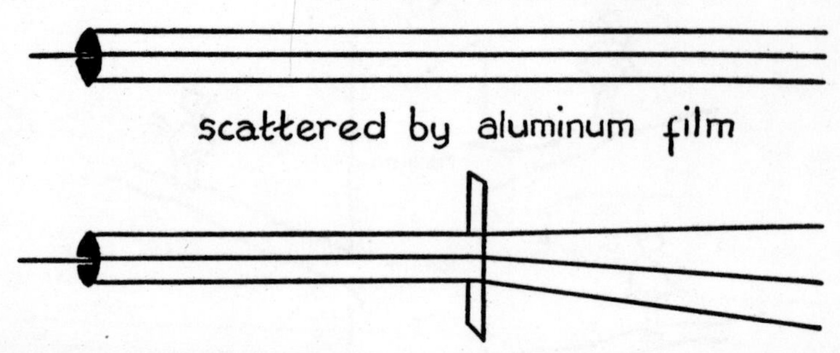

after the scattering experiments he returned to his native Germany, and in 1913 Chadwick followed to work with Geiger. Unfortunately the war intervened, and Chadwick was interned in a German camp. Geiger, however, provided him with apparatus, and with the aid of some fellow prisoners, Chadwick continued to work on radioactivity during the war. Rutherford had already found that when a beam of beta particles fell on one side of a metal plate some of the particles were scattered back on the same side of the plate, like light from a mirror. Light from a mirror is reflected from the mirror surface, but the scattered electrons were reflected from the atoms within the metal plate. No back scattering had ever been observed for alpha particles, so Geiger and Marsden decided to search for alpha particles scattered back at angles greater than 90°. The apparatus used in their investigations was surprisingly simple. A radioactive source of alpha particles was placed at an angle of 45° to the scattering plate. The scattered radiation was observed on a screen also placed at an angle of 45° to the scattering plate, so that the rays could travel in a direct path from the source to the plate and back to the screen. The alpha particles observed were those which had made a right angle turn in the plate. Each alpha particle impinging on the zinc sulphide coated screen produced a bright green scintillation, like those on a luminous watch dial; these

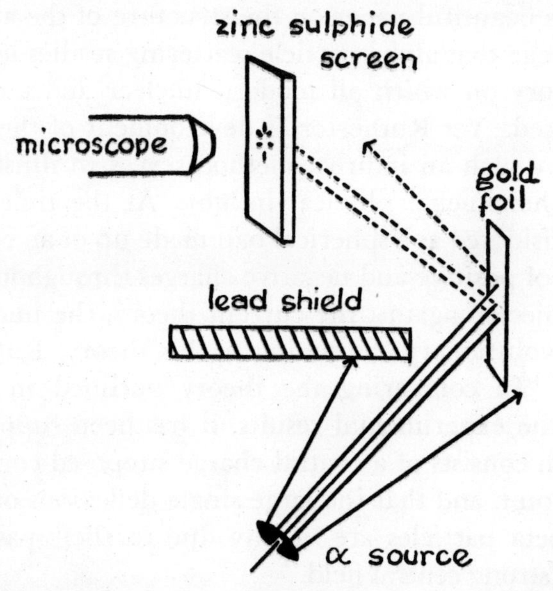

scintillations, counted with the aid of a small microscope, gave a direct measure of the amount of radiation reflected from the scatterer. After the provision of a lead shield to protect the detecting screen from any direct radiation from the source, the apparatus was complete. With the thin foils of gold that Geiger and Marsden used as scattering plate, it was most astonishing that any particles were reflected through so large an angle, since such foil is almost completely transparent to the alpha radiation. Geiger and Marsden reported that, "Compared with the thickness of gold which an alpha particle can penetrate, the effect is confined to a relatively thin layer. . . . If the high velocity and mass of the alpha particle be taken into account, it seems surprising that some of the alpha particles, as the experiment shows, can be turned within a layer of 0.00006 centimeters of gold through an angle of 90° and even more. To produce a similar effect by a magnetic field, the enormous field of one billion absolute units would be required."

These were the results which led Rutherford in 1911 to bring out his beautiful paper on the structure of the atom. It seems strange that alpha particle scattering studies led to this, the theory on which all modern nuclear and atomic physics is based. Yet Rutherford's development of the nucleus atom by such an indirect method serves to illustrate his almost phenomenal physical insight. At the time the atom was considered as a spherical ball made up of an equal distribution of positive and negative charges throughout its volume. Projected against the current theory, the nucleus atom was revolutionary. Summing up his theory, Rutherford wrote: "In comparing the theory outlined in this paper with the experimental results, it has been supposed that the atom consists of a central charge supposed concentrated at a point, and that the large single deflexions of the alpha and beta particles are mainly due to their passage through the strong central field."

Geiger and Marsden had already commented on the intense force necessary to bring about the deflection of the alpha particles that they had observed. The concept of an atom which had a great concentration of charge at one single point, the nucleus, provided just such a strong force. Rutherford had, in fact, developed his theory from a mathematical calculation of the interaction which would exist between an alpha particle and a spherical atom with an intense positive charge concentrated at its center. Associated with the charge, almost the entire mass of the atom is compressed in the nucleus. In the theory the actual shape of the atom is unimportant; it is only important that the charge be concentrated in a central nucleus. The nucleus atom model also explained the scattering of beta particles;

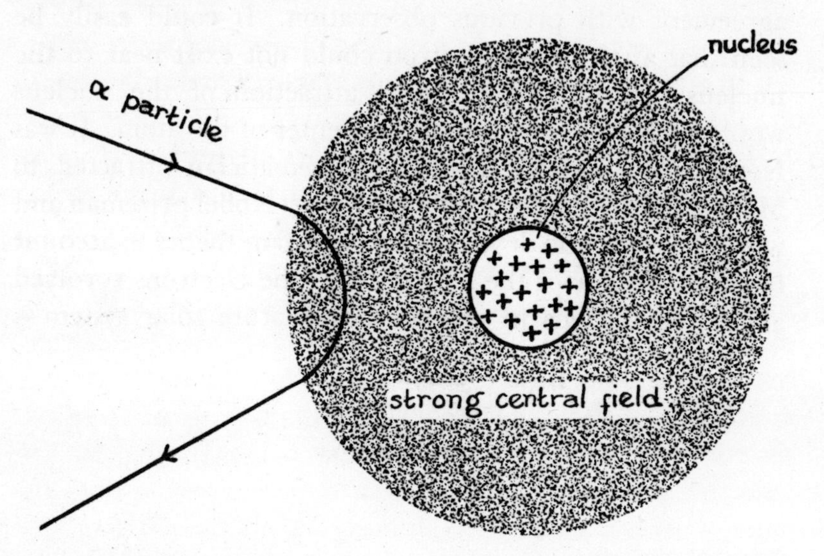

nonetheless Rutherford emphasized the necessity for further experimental check.

This check was provided by Geiger and Marsden, whose painstaking work was not completed until 1913, when they wrote, "At the suggestion of Professor Rutherford we have carried out experiments to test the main conclusions of the above theory. . . . All the measurements have been carried out by observing the scintillations due to the scattered alpha particles on a zinc sulphide screen, and during the course of the experiments over 100,000 scintillations have been counted. . . . All the results of our investigations are in good agreement with the theoretical deductions of Professor Rutherford, and afford strong evidence of the correctness of the underlying assumption that an atom contains a strong charge at its centre, of dimensions small compared with the diameter of the atom."

The theory of the nucleus atom left unexplained the disposition of the electrons around the nucleus. Some electrons were necessary to compensate for the strong positive nuclear charge so that the atom should be neutral electrically in agreement with previous observation. It could easily be seen that a stationary electron could not exist near to the nucleus because the electrical attraction of the nucleus would suck the electron into the center of the atom. It was Niels Bohr, a young Danish mathematician attracted to Manchester by Rutherford's work, now Nobel prizeman and world-famous, who developed the brilliant theory to account for the behavior of the electrons. If the electrons revolved about the nucleus in orbits — a miniature solar system —

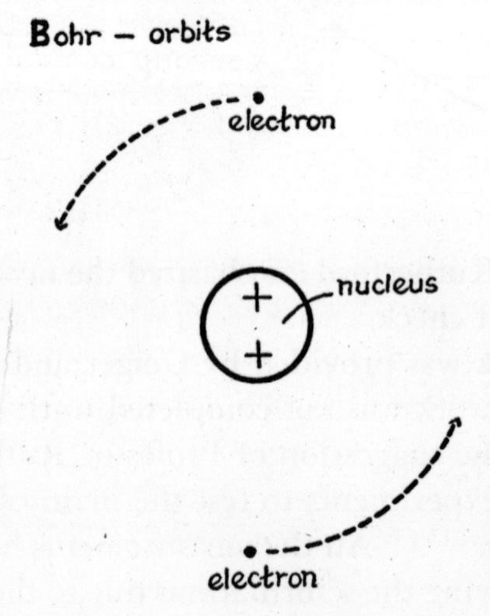

then the atom could be stable. Under these conditions it was easily possible for each atom to contain a number of electrons great enough exactly to counterbalance the positive charge on the nucleus. The only requirement on the electrons was for them to revolve constantly in their orbits, as the earth around the sun.

Rutherford's theory demanded that the nucleus must be small compared with the size of the atom; and investigation of the hydrogen atom bears out the prediction. The hydrogen atom, the lightest of all atoms, consists of a single proton and a single electron. The electron revolves in a distant orbit around the massive nuclear proton. The area that the electron sweeps out in its path, the outer boundary of the hydrogen atom, has a diameter even less than one hundred millionth of an inch. But the proton carrying all the mass of the atom has a diameter of only about one million millionth of an inch. This means that the diameter of the proton is one ten thousandth of the diameter of the atom; all the extra-nuclear volume is given over to the peregrinations of a single electron.

As it is with the hydrogen atom, so it is with all the other atoms. But the simplicity of hydrogen with its single electron gives way to greater and greater complexity as the weight and the nuclear charge of the atoms increase. The nucleus atom is not a simple atom; the symmetry of equal distribution of charge and mass throughout a sphere has given way before the ordered complexity of nucleus and electrons. Becquerel's discovery had led to a new conception of the nucleus – Rutherford's work, based for the first time on a clearly defined atom, tested and confirmed by experiment, provided an important and vital beginning in understanding the structure of matter.

CHAPTER 5

THE ATOMIC NUMBER

JUST three months after Geiger and Marsden's brilliant confirmation of Rutherford's nucleus atom, Moseley and Darwin published their original paper on the reflections of x-rays from crystals. This paper – the only one in which Darwin, a grandson of Charles Darwin and now head of the National Physical Laboratory in London, collaborated – was the first of a series of three papers which comprised a detailed examination of the properties of x-rays. Moseley, when still an undergraduate at Oxford, had come to Manchester to seek permission to work in Rutherford's laboratory after graduation. There can be no doubt that Rutherford possessed to an extraordinary degree the power to collect around him, and to inspire men of outstanding ability. Moseley was so exceptional that every author who mentions him, or his work, always makes a point of commenting on the brilliance of this young physicist. The clarity of his insight remains astonishing even today when all the results of his experiments are accepted as a matter of fact. Shortly after coming to Manchester, Moseley began his x-ray research, and the first two papers appeared from Manchester. The third, published in April, 1914, from Oxford where Moseley's original apparatus is still preserved, was to be his last. Five months later England declared war, and in the summer of 1915 Moseley, then only 27 years old, was killed at Gallipoli.

X-radiation is closely connected with those electron beams which have been, directly or indirectly, responsible for so many of the advances of physics; in fact, x-radiation is that radiation produced when a fast moving beam of electrons

An early photograph of Lord Rutherford.

Keystone-Underwood

In 1932, shortly after Cockcroft and Walton had achieved the first artificial transmutation, this photograph of Lord Rutherford and Walton was taken in front of the Cavendish laboratory

H. G. J. Moseley, before World War I.

impinges on a target and comes to a sudden stop. When the electron, traveling at great speed, stops dead in its tracks, it must give off its energy of motion in some fashion; and it gives off some of the energy as x-radiation. So a flint, when striking steel, gives off part of its energy of motion as a spark. X-radiation, like gamma rays and light, is non-corpuscular and travels with the velocity of light. But the energy of the x-rays, their power to penetrate matter, depends entirely on the energy of the electrons which have given rise to the radiation. X-radiation produced by 1,000,000 volt electrons is much more penetrating than that produced by thousand-volt electrons. Part of this radiation is independent of the target the electron hits, much as the quality of the spark is independent of the steel the flint is struck against.

There is, though, a second sort of x-radiation which is characteristic of the electron target, and it was this radiation that interested Moseley. Hitherto it had not been possible to measure the wave length of the x-radiation. The radiation of a beam of light, however, can be analysed into its component parts by a spectroscope, so that all the light of one specific color, that is, wave length, falls on one specific part of a screen, or photographic plate. In a spectroscope it is a prism, or a grating, a piece of metal with lines closely spaced and accurately ruled on to its surface, that is responsible for the analysis of light into its various components. For x-rays no prisms were available, and the requirements for a grating specified lines so close together that it was impossible to rule them. However, in 1912 it was suggested that the atoms in certain crystals, packed tightly and regularly, each next the other, would serve as a grating for x-ray analysis.

Seizing upon this discovery, Moseley immediately set to work to build an x-ray spectroscope. Moseley's original apparatus was so like an ordinary spectroscope that he constructed it from the parts of a discarded one. At one end of the spectroscope, corresponding to the source of light, there was an x-ray tube. In this tube electrons emitted from a hot cathode were driven towards the anode in a strong electric field. The electrons produced x-rays when they struck the anode, and these in turn, projected at a right angle to the

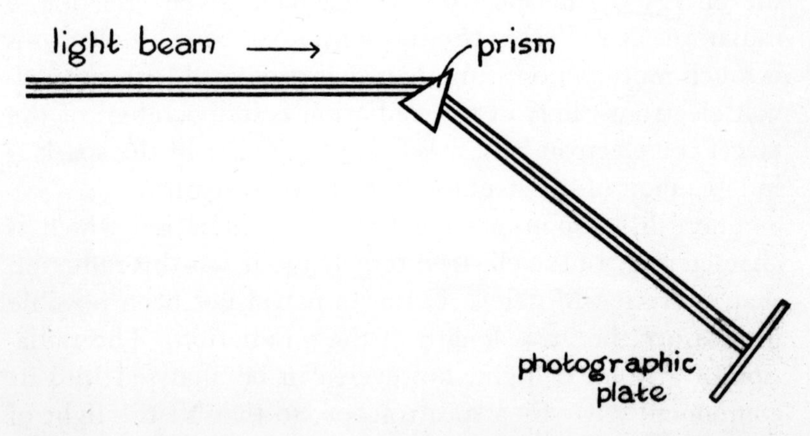

incident electron beam, passed through two diaphragms before reaching the crystal scatterer as a sharply defined beam. From the crystal the x-rays were scattered to a detector which registered the intensity of the rays. Both the crystal and the detector could be rotated about a common axis, and so it was possible to compare the x-radiation scattered at various angles with the initial beam. Moseley found, as had been predicted and already observed by others, that at certain angles the reflected beam was especially intense. From the angles at which this intensity was greatest and from the constants of the crystal it was easily possible to calculate the wave length of the x-radiation responsible. In this manner Moseley found five different wave lengths of homogeneous, that is "monochromatic" x-rays, which he ascribed to the platinum anode in the x-ray tube. Although the work done was painstaking and accurate, no novel results had yet appeared.

There was a great difference between the radiation from the general collision of the electron beam with a target, and the monochromatic radiation measured by Moseley. The

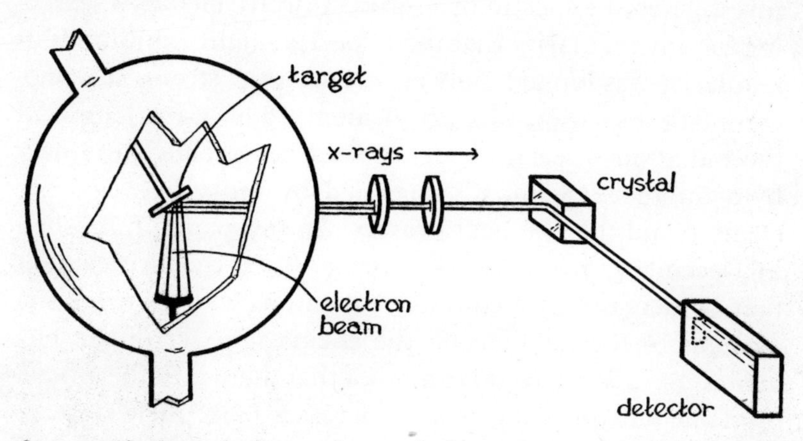

first radiation, independent of the target, was not homogeneous in any way. The x-rays produced had wave lengths of all sorts varying up to a maximum determined by the speed of the electron beam. Such radiation is often called "white" radiation for, like white light, it is made up of many component parts. But the second radiation, called monochromatic, is similar to one specific shade of a color. Electrons responsible for this characteristic radiation, in impinging on the target, knock one of the electrons loose from a platinum atom. When now another electron falls into the hole, the platinum atom emits its characteristic radiation. Since such radiation arises from filling a need in the platinum atom itself, it is characteristic not only of the platinum atom, but also of the specific need which the electron fills.

In his second paper Moseley deduced the relationship of

the monochromatic x-radiation to the structure of the atom producing it. After his work with platinum, he used other elements as anode in his x-ray tube. The main improvement in technique of these later experiments was the substitution of a photographic plate for the earlier electrical detector, as well as a somewhat better geometrical arrangement of the components. With this apparatus Moseley investigated the spectra of a series of twelve elements searching for any regularity that these spectra might exhibit. This regularity was immediately apparent in the strongest monochromatic radiation of each element. The wave length of the radiation of each element could be specified uniquely by a number, Q, and Q increased by unity between any element and the one next heavier. In this paper, published in December, 1913, Moseley wrote, "It is at once evident that Q increases by a constant amount as we pass from one element to the next, using the chemical order of the elements. . . . We have here a proof that there is in the atom a fundamental quantity, which increases by regular steps as we pass from one element to the next. This quantity can only be the charge on the central positive nucleus of the existence of which we already have definite proof."

The reasoning underlying this explanation is clear and compelling. Moseley had already seen that the radiation came about as a consequence of the ejection of an electron from the atom. The position and properties of such an electron revolving about a charged nucleus are clearly determined by the charge on the nucleus. Consequently, it is to be expected that the radiation given off when another electron falls into the space left by an ejected electron should be characteristic of the charge on the nucleus. In his final paper, published in April of 1914, Moseley extended his results by the detailed examination of the spectra of 46 separate elements. Then came Gallipoli.

Moseley's extraordinary work cleared up numerous unexplained points about the nuclear atom. By 1913 chemical analysis had given the chemical masses of most of the elements, and the elements had been arranged in tabular form according to ascending values of the chemical mass, and then numbered in the same order. Thus the atomic number was 1 for hydrogen, 2 for helium, the next heavier element, and so on up. Moseley immediately connected his value of

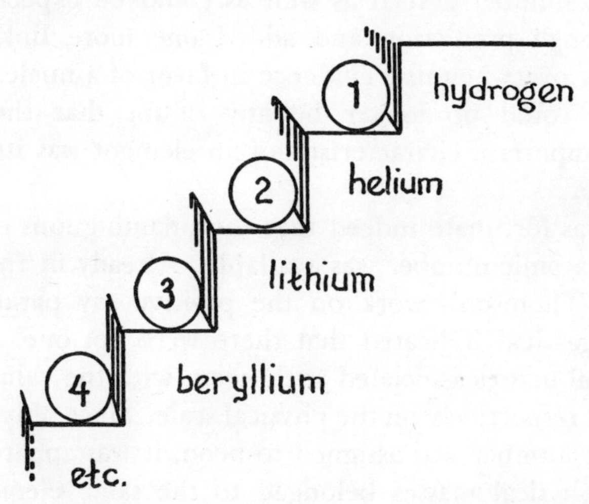

Q with the atomic number and showed that the progression of atomic number and atomic weight were almost identical. In some few exceptional cases, Moseley found that his atomic number differed from the order of chemical weights, but he was able to show that the chemical properties of the element demanded that its order be that given by the atomic number – that, in fact, the chemical weight was relatively unimportant compared with the atomic number. In some exceptional cases a space in the progression indicated the position of an undiscovered element; hafnium for example, discovered since Moseley's time, fits as expected into its place in the atomic number series.

Another and equally important correlation was that between the atomic number and the charge on the nucleus. At Rutherford's request Geiger and Marsden had examined the scattering by elements of increasing chemical weight. The results indicated that the nuclear charge responsible for the scattering increased with increasing weight; and Geiger and Marsden showed that the value of the nuclear charge was approximately one half that of the chemical weight. Moseley's discovery of the exact atomic number agreed as well as could be expected with this rough prediction and added one more link to the already overwhelming evidence in favor of a nuclear atom. There could no longer be any doubt that the single most important characteristic of an element was its atomic number.

It was fortunate indeed that the unambiguous criterion of the atomic number was available. Already in 1913, Professor Thomson's work on the positive ray parabolas of neon gas had indicated that there were not one, but two physical masses associated with neon, with the values of 20 and 22 respectively on the physical scale. Since only a single atomic number was assigned to neon, it was apparent that both physical masses belonged to the same element. In addition, the chemical weight, which should exactly equal the physical weight if both determinations are accurate, had been determined very accurately as 20.2. In order to explain this phenomenon it was necessary to assume that there could be two forms of the same element possessing the same atomic number and identical chemical properties, varying only in the mass of each form. So two twins can be identical in face, height, color of hair, and all noticeable physical properties, yet differ by a few pounds in weight. On such a view ordinary neon was composed largely of neon of mass 20, with an admixture of enough heavier neon of mass 22 to bring the average chemical weight up to 20.2. To describe such atomic twins, Frederic Soddy – the chemist who had done such excellent work with Rutherford in the early days of radioactivity – proposed the name isotope. Isotopes were already known in the radioactive families where, in order to explain the multiplicity of elements, it had been necessary to assume the existence of some elements having identical atomic number and different atomic weight. The isotopes of neon are separable only by delicate physical means, un-

known in 1913. Since nature does not have the equipment to separate isotopes on earth, neon as it occurs naturally always consists of the same proportion of isotopes and always has a chemical mass of 20.2.

With the development of Aston's mass-spectrograph after World War I, the discovery of isotopes followed in quick succession. Elements such as tin are now known to have as many as ten isotopes, while sodium on the other hand has but one. It was the concept of isotopes which showed the identity of chemical and physical measurements of mass. Wherever any chemical measurements indicated an average mass value that was not a whole number, there was always an isotope to account for the deviation. When Prout proposed his hypothesis in 1815 chemical evidence rejected it as untenable; when Rutherford proposed the fundamental nature of the proton in 1920, the pioneer work of Moseley had paved the way.

CHAPTER 6

THE NUCLEUS

In the Bakerian lecture in 1920, Rutherford had proposed a nucleus constructed out of protons and electrons. With the addition of other aggregate particles such a nuclear model served until the discovery of the neutron. Shortly afterwards it was suggested on theoretical grounds that the atomic nucleus could be best imagined in terms of neutron and proton. According to this view the nucleus is essentially a simple structure, built up out of neutrons and protons very much like a house built by a child out of two kinds of colored blocks. The neutrons serve to provide mass where it is needed and the protons to provide the necessary

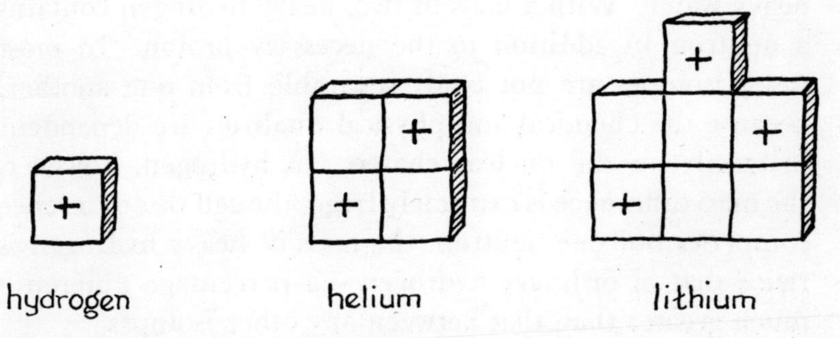

nuclear charge. With all the blocks having unit value, the neutron unit mass, and the proton unit mass and unit charge, it is only necessary to put the blocks together in the right way.

Hydrogen is the simplest element, for its nucleus is a single proton. The next heavier element is helium, which has the next higher number on the atomic number scale.

That is, the nuclear charge must be two; so two protons are required. But the mass of helium is four, hence the nucleus must also contain two neutrons to give the additional weight. With lithium, the lightest metal, which has a charge of three and a mass of seven, three protons and four neutrons are needed. From these results a general rule may be formulated which states that the number of protons in any nucleus is exactly equal to the atomic number or nuclear charge. Then the number of neutrons must equal the weight of the atom less the number of protons, that is, the nuclear mass minus the nuclear charge. This rule is completely general and may be applied to any nucleus.

In such a scheme the construction of isotopes is easily explicable. From Aston and Moseley's work isotopes are known to have the same charge, differing only in mass. Then from the rule above it is seen that all the isotopes of an element have exactly the same number of protons and differ only in the number of neutrons. Hydrogen has a heavy isotope, the deuteron which provides the "heavy" in heavy water. With a mass of two, heavy hydrogen contains a neutron in addition to the necessary proton. In most cases, isotopes are not easily separable from one another, because the chemical and physical qualities are dependent primarily on the nuclear charge. In hydrogen, however, the mass difference is extremely large; though this difference comprises but one neutron, the mass of heavy hydrogen is twice that of ordinary hydrogen – a percentage difference much greater than that between any other isotopes.

The separation of heavy hydrogen from normal hydrogen in which it is present to the extent of only 0.02 per cent can be achieved by taking advantage of the great difference in weight between the isotopes. When an electrical current is passed through water, the water is dissociated and the hydrogen gas bubbles off at the negative electrode. As the bubbles pass through the liquid, the ordinary hydrogen comes off in the gas and the heavy hydrogen remains behind in the liquid. After many repetitions of the process water may be obtained in which the hydrogen is more than 99 per cent heavy hydrogen. When this discovery was made there was an immediate demand for water from old storage batteries, rich in heavy hydrogen from repeated passage of electricity for many years. The demand for heavy hydrogen in scientific laboratories is so great that it is now produced commercially and marketed, like other rare gases, in small pressure tanks.

The nuclei of heavier isotopes are made up in exactly the same way, although in these cases the difference of one

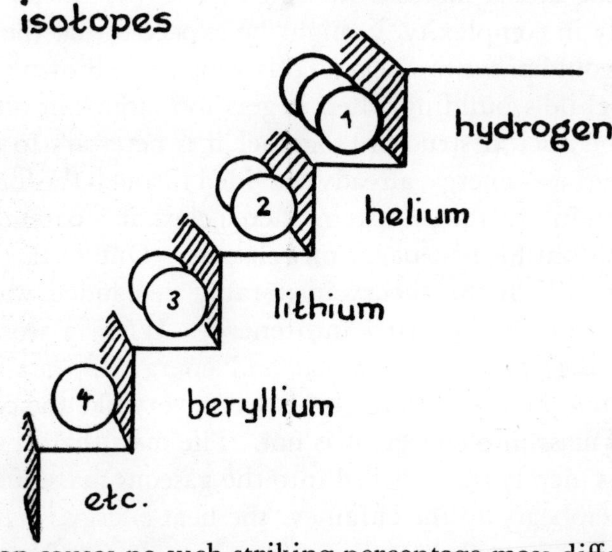

neutron causes no such striking percentage mass difference. Helium has two stable isotopes and lithium two also with masses of 6 and 7. The nuclear charge on lithium being three, the light isotope is composed of three each of protons and neutrons, while the ordinary isotope of mass 7 contains one additional neutron. The same structure is evident in elements having many isotopes like iron which, with a charge of 26, has isotopes of masses 54, 56, 57, and 58. So the iron nucleus must contain 26 protons, and of the four isotopes, one must contain 28 neutrons, one 30, one 31, and one 32. Even tin with ten isotopes is put together in exactly the same fashion.

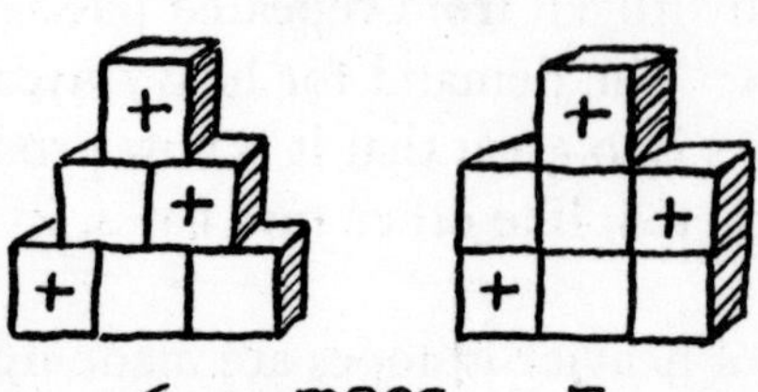

As the atoms increase in weight, and the nuclei consequently in complexity, it might be expected that the structures would prove top-heavy, collapsing of their own weight, like a child's building when it gets too large. In order to hold the nuclear structure together it is necessary to use an atomic glue — energy, already provided through the foresight of Einstein. In 1905 Einstein, then a clerk in a patent office, brought out his first paper on relativity. One of the consequences which the theory inexorably demanded was that mass could be converted into energy. When a wood fire burns, the wood is consumed and energy appears as the heat from the fire: although this seems very like the conversion of mass into energy, it is not. The mass that was solid wood is merely transformed into the gaseous mass of smoke and disappears up the chimney: the heat energy is not produced by any real change in mass. The electron, however, provides a true conversion of mass into energy, for it is possible to burn the electron so completely that it disappears entirely. Then all that remains for a wreath of smoke is the energy liberated upon consumption of the electron.

The energy which appears when an electron is converted is one half of a million electron volts; energy similarly reclaimed from nuclear mass binds the nucleus together.

F. W. Goro for Life Magazine

Albert Einstein.

Ivory Photo

Million volt linked transformer generator at the University of Michigan. The column of linked transformers is on the right, and the accelerating tube on the left.

The term million electron volt — the energy of one electron after it has fallen through an electric field of 1,000,000 volts — is a convenient and picturesque term to use in describing the energies available in nuclei. Such a large unit is necessary because the energies involved are themselves tremendous.

A considerable energy is released in the coalescence of the constituent elements of a particle so simple as the deuteron. The proton has a mass of 1.0076 units, and the neutron 1.0090. The masses of these particles are greater than the unit mass by small, but nonetheless real amounts — an apparent violation of the principle that all nuclei are made up from particles of unit mass. This apparent violation is in effect the provision of the atomic glue, for the excess of mass is burned to provide the energy which holds the nucleus together. The sum of the masses of proton and neutron is 2.0166, while the mass of the deuteron, made up from these particles, is 2.0142. The difference in mass corresponds to an energy of 2,200,000 electron volts, the energy liberated when the two particles come together to form a deuteron. This deficit must be supplied to separate the particles again: the higher the deficit, the more energy is required to break up a nucleus. The sum of the masses of the components in the helium nucleus, or alpha particle, comes to 4.0332 mass units, while the actual mass of the helium is only 4.0027 units. In this case there is a very large mass available for conversion into energy, and the binding energy of the alpha particle is 28,000,000 electron volts. Such a high binding energy corresponds to a very stable nucleus, and is the explanation for the especial stability of the alpha particle.

A nucleus composed of neutrons and protons confirms the fundamental nature of these particles; an atom composed of a heavy positively charged nucleus, surrounded by a cloud of electrons, offers as well an explanation of the behavior of these and other particles as they pass through matter. The nucleus is so small a part of the atom that particles seldom collide with it; perhaps one particle in a million may actually hit a nucleus. All the other charged particles dissipate their energy among the electrons which wheel in their orbits around the nuclei. Deuteron and proton, both charged, are brought to a rapid stop by this electrical braking system. But the neutron, uncharged, is unaffected by the electrons and can pass right by them. A neutron is only slowed down by an intimate collision with a nucleus, and then only slowed down appreciably if it hits a nucleus its own size, like hydrogen. Consequently it will pass through a three foot wall of lead with far greater facility than through a three foot tank of water.

With the nucleus atom, the atomic number, the proton, and the neutron, the concept of the atom has been considerably clarified since Thomson's first experiments on cathode rays. This progress, like all progress in science, has come not from a frontal attack on the nucleus itself, but rather by a series of steps, some directly connected with the problem, some at the beginning only distantly related to it. Even the achievement of each step is not always the direct result of long and painstaking work in a single direction. Often work of this character, brilliant in concept and execution, has brought out results of fundamental importance. But often work in an apparently unrelated field has produced results which also, with a sudden clear flash of insight, become directly related to the problem. In science it is impossible to work directly towards a given large goal, for no one can predict what new discoveries may occur along the way, to change and modify the original object. Yet, looking backwards, the present concept of the nuclear atom may be said to owe its development to one single man, working, thinking, encouraging others; and that man is Rutherford.

PART II
HOW SMASH THE ATOM?

CHAPTER 7

TRANSMUTATION

THE atom makes use of a powerful defense in protecting its integrity. Outposts far from the massive nucleus, the light electrons whirl in their orbits. An invading particle aimed at the nucleus is undisturbed by these outer fringes of defense and passes easily through them into the great volume of empty space surrounding the nucleus. Only when it approaches the heavy core itself do the forces that guard the atom come into play. All around the nucleus there is an intense, repulsive electrical field. The deeper the invading particle penetrates the field, the more strongly it is repelled. When still far from the nucleus, though well within the electron orbits, the electrical forces are negligible, but as the particle approaches the nucleus closely, the forces become important and it is repelled. The experiments on scattering from which Rutherford deduced the nucleus atom showed that these forces were strong enough to send alpha particles back whence they came.

Little wonder that the alchemists were unable to transmute an atom so well-protected. The weapons which they possessed were completely inadequate for a job of such magnitude. Finally, in 1919, the weapon that Rutherford had used to probe the atom and discover the nucleus, he used again to probe the nucleus itself. By then the alpha particle was almost twenty-five years old, yet Rutherford was the first man to seize upon it and use it to achieve transmutation, when for the first time he showed that man could truly change the nature of an atom.

In July of 1919, Rutherford, shortly after he had succeeded Sir J. J. Thomson as Cavendish Professor at Cambridge, published his results on the interaction of alpha particles with gases. In this, as in so much of Rutherford's work, the apparatus was simple in the extreme. A radioactive alpha particle source was placed in a box closed at one

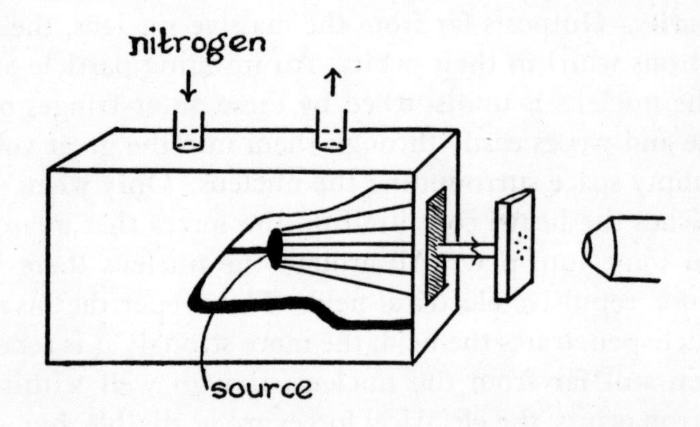

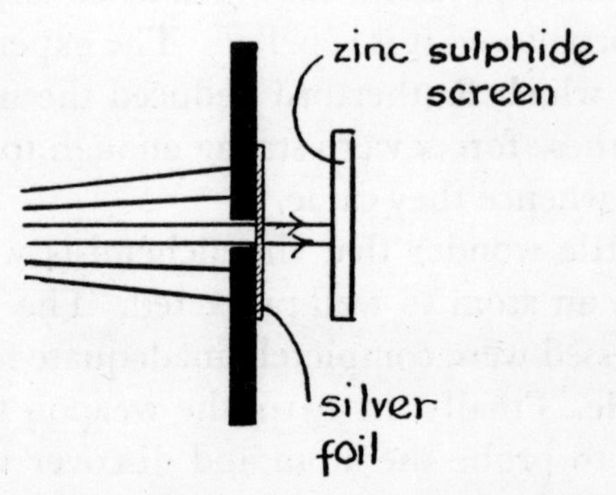

end with a thin silver foil which the particles could penetrate easily. Passing through the foil the rays fell on a zinc sulphide screen. When the box was filled with dry oxygen, enough additional foil was placed between the source and the screen to absorb all the alpha radiation: no particles impinged on the screen. But if the oxygen was removed and dry nitrogen substituted, scintillations immediately appeared. The only possible interpretation was that the alpha particles, acting on the nitrogen nuclei in the gas, entered into a nuclear reaction which produced particles more penetrating than the original alpha particles. To identify these penetrating particles the box was placed in a magnetic field. Using a simple adaptation of the method of analysis employed by J. J. Thomson in establishing the nature of positive rays, Rutherford proved that the particles from the nitrogen were protons. This result was explicable only by the transmutation of nitrogen.

An alpha particle in close collision with a nitrogen nucleus had expelled a proton from that nucleus. The ejection of the proton corresponded to a change in nuclear charge in Moseley's atomic number system: the element produced had to be different from the bombarded nitrogen. Rutherford himself wrote, "We must conclude that the nitrogen atom is disintegrated under the intense forces developed in a close collision with a swift alpha particle, and that the hydrogen atom which is liberated formed a constituent part of the nitrogen nucleus."

In order to understand how an alpha particle can enter into a nitrogen nucleus, it is necessary to understand first how an alpha particle is projected from a radioactive element. The radioactive elements, of which there are about 40 isotopes, are the heaviest known elements, radium being heavier even than lead. With such a heavy element and, therefore, so complex a nucleus it is natural to expect tremendous forces concentrated inside the nucleus. The radium nucleus may be considered as a volcano with neutrons and protons stewing violently inside the crater. Occasionally there is an eruption and an alpha particle, a particularly stable combination of two protons and two neutrons that is sometimes considered to exist as a whole in the nucleus, is ejected. While in an ordinary volcano the lava is spewed out over the top, in a radioactive one theory has shown that the alpha particle can more easily tunnel its way through the side of the mountain. The particle would get out over the top if it could, but it possesses only enough energy to burrow its way through the hillside. The same

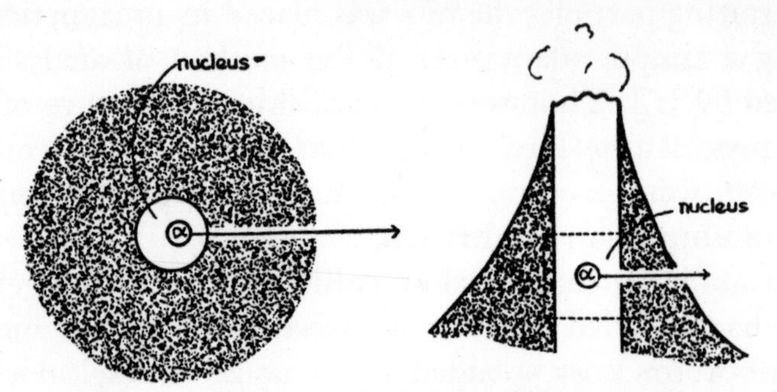

alpha particle emitted by tunnelling through barrier

mountain slope which keeps the particles inside the nucleus also protects the nucleus from invasion by foreign particles. The alpha particle to escape from the nucleus must have energy enough to tunnel its way free; on the other hand, a successful invading particle must be strong enough to climb over the rim of the volcano. The invading particle can very seldom find a place to tunnel through; most of the successful invasions are carried out by attacks over the top.

As of Vesuvius, it is impossible to predict when a specific atomic explosion will occur. Since an atom is very small, there are enough of them in any measurable volume so that the laws of statistics may be applied. That is, although the exact time when one given radium atom will explode can not be specified, it is possible to say with a high degree of accuracy that one half of the atoms of a quantity of radium will have exploded in 1690 years, one half of those that are left will have exploded in the next 1690 years, and so on until eternity. Radium is neither the longest, nor the shortest living radioactive element, for with uranium only half of the eruptions occur in each five billion years. With radium C′ on the other hand, half is disintegrated in about one ten thousandth of a second, and the cycle has repeated itself almost ten thousand times by the time a second has elapsed. It is one of the most interesting facts of radioactivity that nothing man can do is able to influence in any way the rate at which the radioactive elements decompose. Neither the highest temperature attainable on earth, nor the greatest possible cold can alter the rate of radioactive decomposition.

The energy of the ejected alpha particle is dependent on the nature of the radioactive element emitting it. There are only ten heavy radioactive elements, yet the complexity of their isotopes is such that there are more than twenty varieties of alpha radiation. The energy of the alpha particle is the energy it receives in rolling down the side of the mountain, an energy clearly dependent on the height of the mountain and the position where the alpha particle tunnels through. The great energy of the alpha particles is due to the height of the mountain, intensified for the alpha particle because it carries a double charge. The hill is so high and the forces so tremendous that alpha particles are known to reach velocities as high as 45,000,000 miles an hour.

Beta radiation, the expulsion of high speed electrons, is neither so clearly explicable nor so well understood as alpha radiation. For one thing the electrons do not exist as independent entities in the nucleus. On theoretical grounds, neutrons are said to be able to change into protons inside the nuclear crater. This change is accompanied by the appearance of an electron, a change which seems somewhat more plausible since the balance of charge remains constant. The negative charge on the electron cancels the positive charge on the proton, totalling zero charge. Any change of mass is converted into energy. It is this change, the neutron-proton conversion, that accounts for the energy which the electron takes with it as it departs. Although the electron energy is always supplied by the same process, the amount of energy liberated is not always the same, depending, as does the alpha radiation, on the exact qualities and arrangement of the particles inside the nucleus before and after emission. A clear explanation of the expulsion and the energies of beta particles has not yet been reached; it remains one of the great unsolved problems of modern physics.

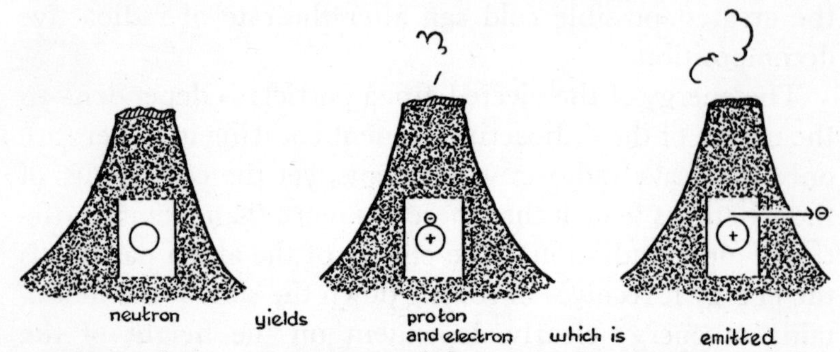

The emission of a beta particle results in a transformation of the nucleus into that of another element. The radiation of an alpha particle means a loss of two protons; in this case the daughter element is two steps lower in the atomic number series than the parent. After emitting an alpha particle, radium, with an atomic number 88 and weight 226, becomes radon, with number 86 and weight 222. The loss of an electron, however, coincides with the formation of a proton from an uncharged particle; in this case, therefore, the daughter element will be one step higher than the parent. The emission of a beta particle from radium B, with number 82 and weight 214 accompanies its transformation into radium C, with number 83 and weight 214. Beta particle emission, however, obeys the same laws of chance that alpha emission does. It is just as impossible to predict when a specific atom will emit a beta particle as an alpha particle. The rate of emission can be found in the same way from the observation of the half-life of the element. Strangely, the range of time in natural beta radioactive elements is not so great as with the alpha emitters; the longest beta emitter, radium D, disintegrates halfway in about 22 years, while the shortest, uranium X_2, takes a whole minute to lose half its particles. As with alpha radiation, man is unable to alter the rate of production of beta particles.

Penetrating gamma radiation, the third radiation given off by natural radioactive elements, is purely an energy radiation. Usually gamma radiation occurs as the accompaniment of either alpha or beta particle emission. It may be that a new element formed after the emission of an alpha or beta particle may find itself excited, that is, with more energy than is normal for such an atom. Except for the energy given off in the expulsion of the particle, the new element has taken over the energy of the parent element completely, an energy which may or may not be compatible with its requirements. Should the energy be too great the daughter element throws off the excess in the form of gamma radiation and returns to a normal state. Gamma rays need not always accompany the emission of alpha and beta particles; unaccompanied particles mean only that the daughter element is energetically content. Gamma radiation usually has no distinctive half-life; occasionally, however, there is a traffic jam in the nucleus and the gamma ray can not escape immediately. In these rare cases the gamma ray makes its way out as best it can, with a half-life determined by the delay in its emission.

The particles which are given off in a nucleus also serve as invader particles, as shown by the disintegration of nitrogen by alpha particles. With Chadwick, Rutherford continued the transmutation experiments, and shortly they were able to report disintegrations of five other elements. Nonetheless, the alpha particle is not a very acceptable weapon. It is heavy and doubly charged: the mountain slope, or potential barrier, around the nucleus core is particularly high for the alpha particle. However, alpha particles, naturally produced from radioactive elements, are readily available endowed with sufficient energy to cross the potential barrier and enter the nucleus.

The proton, on the other hand, is a particle far more feasible for nuclear penetration. Smaller than the alpha particle, it has unit mass and a single charge. Each of these features makes it easy for the proton to gain enough energy to climb the mountain and enter into the nucleus. The charge is a necessary adjunct since, if the protons are to be produced artificially, there must be a handle to get them going.

The neutron seems an ideal particle to use in nuclear attacks. Since the neutron does not interact with the electric field and can easily penetrate the nuclear defenses, it would not have to climb the mountain, but could roll quietly along on the ground, through the mountain, right into the crater. Yet the electrical slipperiness which enables the neutron to penetrate the mountain means, as well, that it is difficult to grasp the neutron to start it rolling towards the mountain.

But in the deuteron, the nucleus of the heavy hydrogen atom, the properties of both proton and neutron are available. The deuteron is bound together far less tightly than the alpha particle; it is able to break up into its components under proper provocation. The deuteron can easily be accelerated and sent on its way towards the nucleus because it possesses a single charge. When it arrives the mountain presents an even larger barrier than for the proton, so the deuteron releases the loosely-bound neutron and lets it roll into the nucleus, while the proton stays harmlessly outside. Even so, the deuteron penetration of the barrier depends on deuteron energy because the higher up the hill it can get before it gives up its neutron, the easier it is for the neutron to get inside. Any hill gets thinner towards the top. If the deuteron has enough energy to go all the way up the hill and fall in over the top, it can penetrate as a whole without losing the neutron. But the most insidious attack consists of loosing the neutron to continue unimpeded.

The nucleus is not in a position to accept the enemy particle undisturbed. With the additional energy contributed by the invading particle, the nucleus finds itself in an abnormal or excited state. Much as the natural radioactive elements give off gamma rays, the nucleus gives off radiation. But far more often than gamma rays it gives off heavy particles, alpha particles, deuterons, protons, or neutrons. The nucleus contributes its excess energy to the outgoing particle, which then can tunnel its way through the barrier and leave the new nucleus in a normal state. The whole process takes place instantaneously. As soon as the invading particle has penetrated into the nucleus the outgoing particle is sent on its way — the excited state lasts only long enough to communicate the energy to the outgoing particle. The product nucleus is determined not only by the nature of the incoming particle and the initial nucleus, but by the outgoing particle as well. In Rutherford's initial experiment on nitrogen, the nucleus received an alpha particle, a gain of two on the atomic number scale, but gave off a proton, immediately losing one of the charges it had gained. The resultant nucleus was only a single place higher in the atomic number series than nitrogen, that is oxygen. Since the difference in mass between the alpha particle and the proton is three units, the resultant oxygen atom should weigh three units more than the nitrogen with a weight of 14. Subsequent research has verified Rutherford's results and shown the product nucleus to be indeed heavy oxygen with a mass of 17.

When an unaccompanied neutron enters a nucleus the case is somewhat different. For one thing, since the neutron penetrates the mountain so easily it might be supposed that it could roll right through, in one side and out the other, without dropping into the core at the center. Professor

Niels Bohr, responsible not only for the original suggestion of the distant electron orbits around the nucleus, but for much important theoretical work since, delights in a simple experiment which demonstrates why this never happens. The equipment necessary is only a small incline, a common saucer, and a handful of marbles. First Professor Bohr sets up the incline with its bottom ending just inside the saucer. Then he puts a single marble at the top of the incline and lets it roll down onto, and across the saucer. Considering the saucer as nucleus, the neutron marble can penetrate

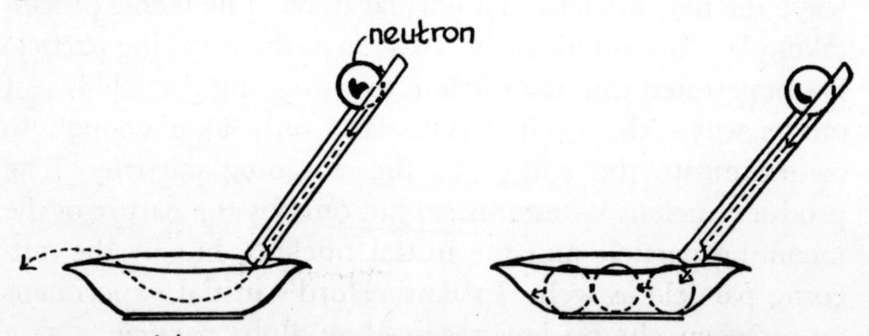

easily into the nucleus and out on the other side. Then he places a handful of marbles inside the saucer, and the neutron marble coming down the incline dissipates its energy by collisions among the marbles already on the saucer. This time the neutron stays in the nucleus, for it has distributed its energy among the particles already inside. With a simple neutron capture the nucleus usually gives out its excess energy by gamma radiation rather than heavy particle emission, probably because it has not sufficient excess energy to expel a particle. Gamma radiation is also often emitted when a proton enters the nucleus; such an emission provides true gamma radiation of energy higher than that observed from natural radioactive elements.

Even though the neutron can not be accelerated directly,

it is of great importance in bombarding nuclei because of the ease with which the nucleus can capture it. The neutrons which are used to bring about disintegration are made on the spot by a previous disintegration. Early workers found that beryllium, bombarded with alpha particles, gave off neutrons: penetration of the nucleus by an alpha particle results in emission of a neutron. The emitted neutrons were used to determine the neutron properties; today they are projectiles themselves.

One requirement for nuclear disintegrations is an adequate supply of bombarding particles. Rutherford pointed out in his early work that the number of effective collisions was very small. It would be possible to hit the traditional needle by firing a machine gun at the haystack, but it would take a long time. The chances of collision between a natural alpha particle and an atomic target are not much greater, for effective collisions do not occur as often as one for each million bombarding particles. A second requirement is that the invading particles, except neutrons, have energy enough to get over the top of the potential barrier or at least well up the hill. The alpha particles used by Rutherford satisfied these requirements, and he became the first scientist to disintegrate elements artificially. For the future it was necessary to provide a more efficient source of atomic projectiles.

CHAPTER 8

ATOM SMASHERS 1 – THE VOLTAGE DOUBLER

By 1932 experiments were under way both in England and America on machines that would produce charged particles with energies great enough to penetrate the nucleus. At the Cavendish, Cockcroft and Walton had adapted a large one-time lecture room for the construction of a high voltage generator. Walton is now at Trinity College in Dublin, Ireland; and Cockcroft, then a young engineer who had found his way into nuclear physics, now holds the Jacksonian Professorship at Cambridge. When the Jacksonian Professorship was originally endowed in 1783, the founder requested that the incumbent "have an eye more particularly to that *opprobrium medicorum* called the gout" – it remains to be seen if nuclear physics will serve as a cure-all. Cockcroft and Walton had already examined the apparatus currently in use for the production of high voltage and had come to the conclusion that no apparatus then available could produce the desired steady beam of high energy particles. At that time the high voltage apparatus was designed either for testing high voltage commercial insulators, or for producing very high energy x-rays. Although million volt x-rays had been produced, unfortunately neither the testing of insulators, nor the production of x-rays for therapeutic use requires that the voltage be applied steadily. These machines, effective as they were for the purpose for which they had been designed, were not easily adaptable to nuclear research.

Nonetheless, some of these generators were used to investigate the nucleus. Voltage can be lowered or raised by a transformer. Some reduce the house voltage to the small fraction used to run toy trains; others can increase the voltage by considerable factors It is impossible to transform a low voltage into one so high as a million volts in one step, because the transformer would spark over inside before the high voltage was reached. However, a set of linked transformers, one attached to the next so that the voltage is increased only a small proportion of the total by each transformer, serves admirably. A million volts can be attained in a reasonable number of steps. These transformers provide voltage for a small percentage of the time, yet this time has been utilized to good advantage in nuclear research.

In another such generator the high voltage can be utilized only for about one thousandth of the time the generator runs. This, the impulse generator, depends only on condensers to reach its high peak voltage. A condenser is a modern adaptation of a Leyden jar, a device already noted in Franklin's time for its ability to store charge. Indeed a simple glass fruit jar coated on the bottom and half way up the side inside and out with tinfoil makes a serviceable Leyden jar, a condenser. When a battery is connected to the Leyden jar with one terminal, say positive, connected to the inner coating, and the other to the outer coating, the condenser is charged to the voltage of the battery. The ability of the Leyden jar to store charge makes it possible for a well-made condenser to retain its charge long after the battery is disconnected. If now the wires from the inside and the outside coatings of the jar are brought close together, a spark will pass with a voltage equal to the voltage of the battery which charged the condenser. A spark equal to twice the voltage of the battery may be obtained by connecting two jars in series. When, after the positive coating of one is attached to the negative coating of the other, the two remaining coatings are brought together a spark with twice the battery voltage will pass. The number of times the voltage can be multiplied depends only on the number of condensers the battery can charge.

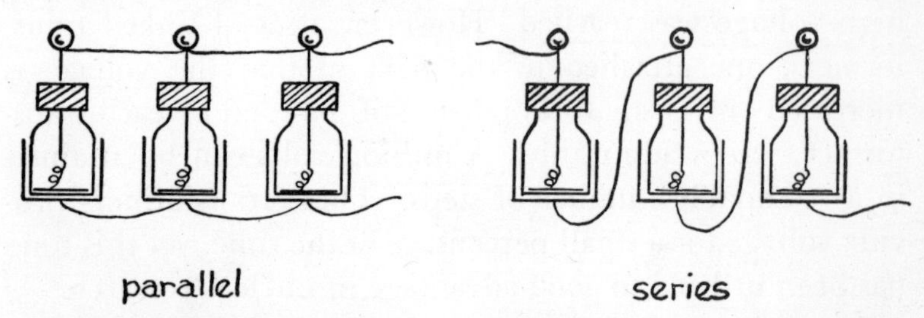

In the impulse generator, condensers in a tower are arranged in parallel so that they can be charged simultaneously. Then each pair of condensers is fitted with a spark gap connecting them in series with the positive side of one

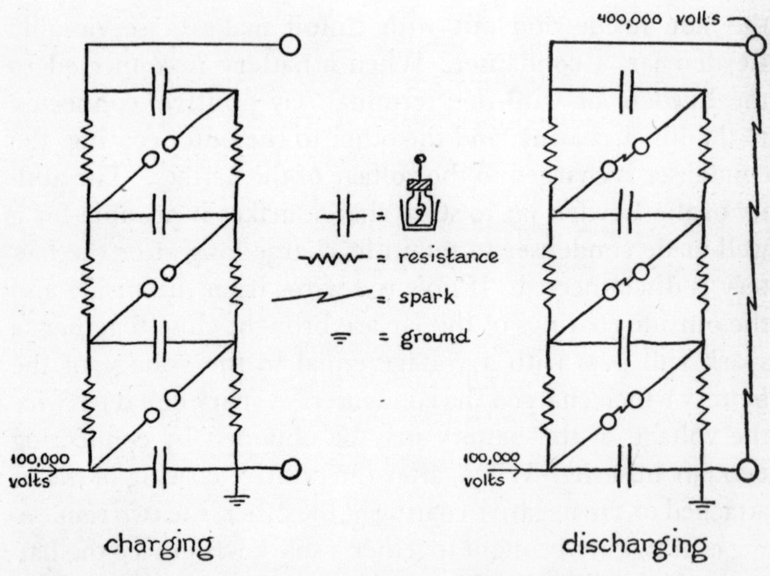

close to the negative side of the other. When the voltage

between the bottom two condensers is high enough to cause a spark across this gap, a spark starts at the bottom of the tower and ripples upwards. It gains in voltage as it passes from condenser to condenser, until finally the voltage of the top condenser is two million volts higher than the bottom one. Now the whole tower gives up its charge in a tremendous two million volt spark. It is like a ball rolling down a flight of stairs gaining energy with each step. The spark itself lasts only for a ten thousandth of a second, and then the whole process of charge, spark-over, and discharge must begin anew. It was this feature of momentary discharge which made the apparatus unsuitable for Cockcroft and Walton. Nonetheless, in spite of its disadvantages, a group of brilliant Austrian scientists used an impulse generator in Vienna with great success in the early days of nuclear research.

The uninterrupted current flow desired by Cockcroft and Walton was secured by the use of a second tower of condensers in their generator. In the impulse generator all the condensers must be discharged instantaneously, because there is no way of controlling the spark that travels upward making the series connection in the tower. However, in the voltage doubler – Cockcroft and Walton's generator – the condensers in one tower are normally connected in series, so that no spark is necessary to discharge them. With such an arrangement a small current may be drawn as long as the condensers are charged. It remains to find a method of charging the tower with the condensers already connected in series. Cockcroft and Walton used a second tower of condensers linked to the first through several rapidly changing switches to solve the problem. The diagram shows a single section in which the voltage is doubled but once. With the switches connected for part 1 of the cycle, the battery charges only condensers A and B, now connected in parallel. When the switches are reversed for part 2 of the cycle, B shares its charge with C. At this point A is fully charged, while B and C are each only half charged. When the switches are returned to the original position, B is recharged. Now when the change is made to part 2, B and C share a charge and a half between them which they divide equally, each retaining three quarters. As the cycles continue C soon becomes fully charged, so that the voltage between the bottom of the tower and the top of C is just double that of the battery.

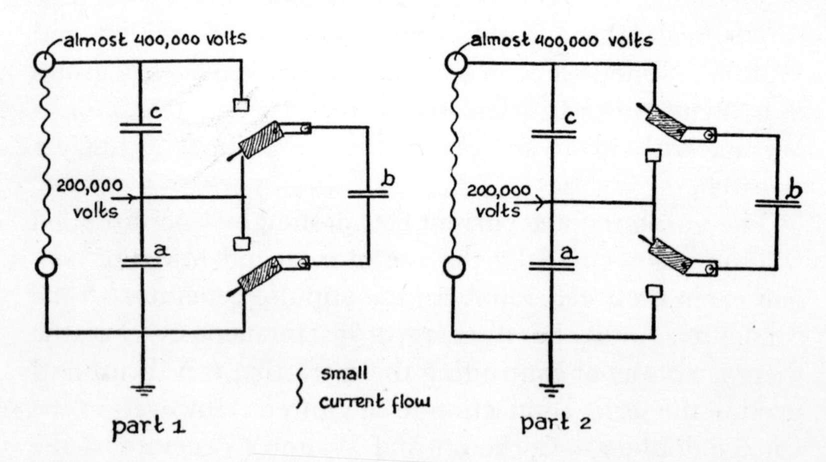

This argument only holds strictly as long as no charge is drained from the A and C tower. If only a small current is drawn A and C will not be completely discharged. A can not be discharged since it is always connected to the battery, and the charge lost by C is immediately replenished from tower B in the second half of the cycle. If the current drawn is small compared with the storing capacity of the condensers, and if the switching action is rapid, it is possible to produce a continuous current at a voltage only slightly less than double the original. The number of condensers in both towers can be increased until the desired voltage is obtained.

Such a system demands a rapid and efficient switching

mechanism that must be completely automatic. Cockcroft and Walton adopted a sophisticated and ingenious system of rectifiers coupled with an alternating current transformer. In ordinary radio sets rectifiers are used to convert to direct current the alternating current that comes from the supply. A rectifier consists only of a hot filament and an anode inside an evacuated tube. Only electrons are present, since there is no gas in the tube; so current can flow only in the direction demanded by the flow of electrons. That is, a rectifier is a one-way valve; electrons will flow from the negative cathode to the positive anode, but not in the reverse direction. If the anode, or plate, is at a higher positive voltage than the cathode, electrons flow, but if the anode is at a lower positive voltage than the cathode, the valve is shut and nothing flows. Thus the condenser A can charge B, and B can charge C, but C can never discharge into B, nor B into A. Since the bottom of B is connected through the condenser D to an alternating current transformer, and since the voltage delivered by the alternating current transformer goes from positive to negative, the voltage at B rises and falls in synchronism. When the voltage is low, B is charged from A, and when the voltage rises, B shares its charge with C. Thus, to begin the cycle, D is first charged directly from the transformer, and the charge is passed on from D to A, from A to B, and so it is ferried all the way up the tower. With apparatus incorporating these features Cockcroft and Walton were able to draw continuous current at voltages as high as 700,000.

However, the achievement of a voltage supply did not solve the problem completely. Nuclear research requires not only high voltage, but also a stream of particles which are accelerated to that high voltage. A positive ray tube filled with hydrogen served as source for the particles. Since all the power available from the voltage doubler was required to accelerate the beam, a subsidiary power supply that would operate in the high voltage region at the top of

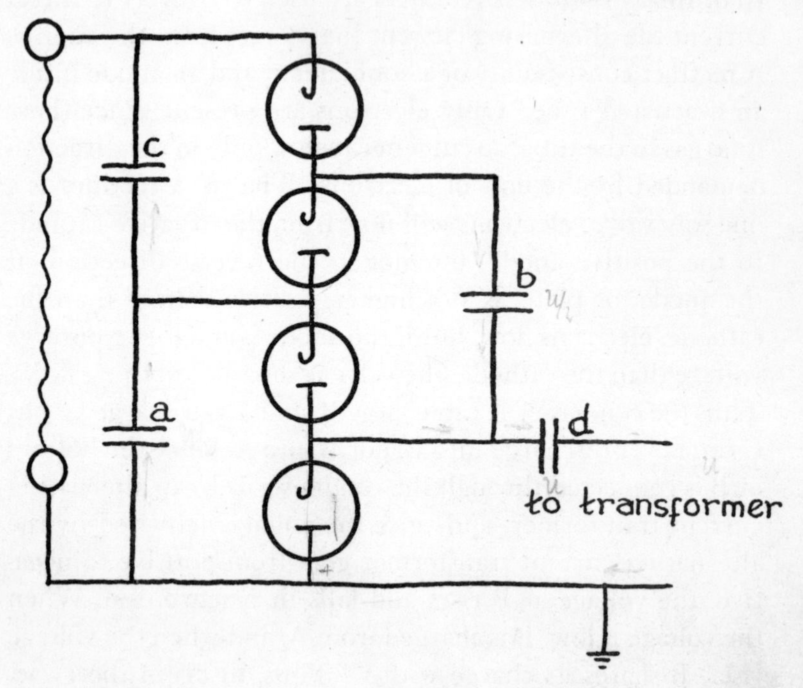

the tube was required to furnish the positive rays. Placed at the high voltage terminal, a small generator driven by cotton pulley rope connected to a motor ten feet away on the ground provided the power. The protons, given a small initial acceleration by the generator power, emerged from the narrow positive ray canal at the top of the accelerating tube. It was not feasible to accelerate the protons in a single step by attraction from the 700,000 volt negative electrode at the top to a grounded plate at the bottom of the tube. Such an arrangement would lead to undue electrical stress inside the tube, as well as a final beam that was not focussed when it arrived at the bottom. Instead, the electrical field was distributed throughout the tube, and the protons were

Reproduced by courtesy of the General Electric Company

A 30-foot spark produced by the 10,000,000 volt impulse generator exhibited at the New York World's Fair in 1939. At the left of the picture the sparks that jump from condenser to condenser ascending the tower can be seen.

Reproduced by courtesy of the General Electric Co.

Close-up of the spark gaps in one of the towers of the General Electric impulse generator.

From the apparatus in the Science Museum, South Kensington, London

The accelerating tube in Cockcroft and Walton's voltage doubler on exhibition in the Science Museum, London. The metal stays that hold the glass tube upright have been added at the museum for safety and form no part of the tube.

accelerated in two steps. Three cylindrical metal electrodes were arranged in a vertical column inside the tube. After emission from the canal, the particles found themselves inside the top electrode at the high voltage. From this, they passed into the middle electrode at an intermediate voltage between 700,000 and ground, and then they entered the bottom electrode.

The protons were accelerated in the regions between the electrodes, that is, in the regions in which there was an intense electrical field. Proper separation of the cylinders provided an electrical focussing effect so that the particles emerged through a thin mica window at the bottom of the tube as a sharply defined, well-focussed beam.

Here they fell either on a fluorescent screen for direct observation, or on a metal target for investigation of nuclear

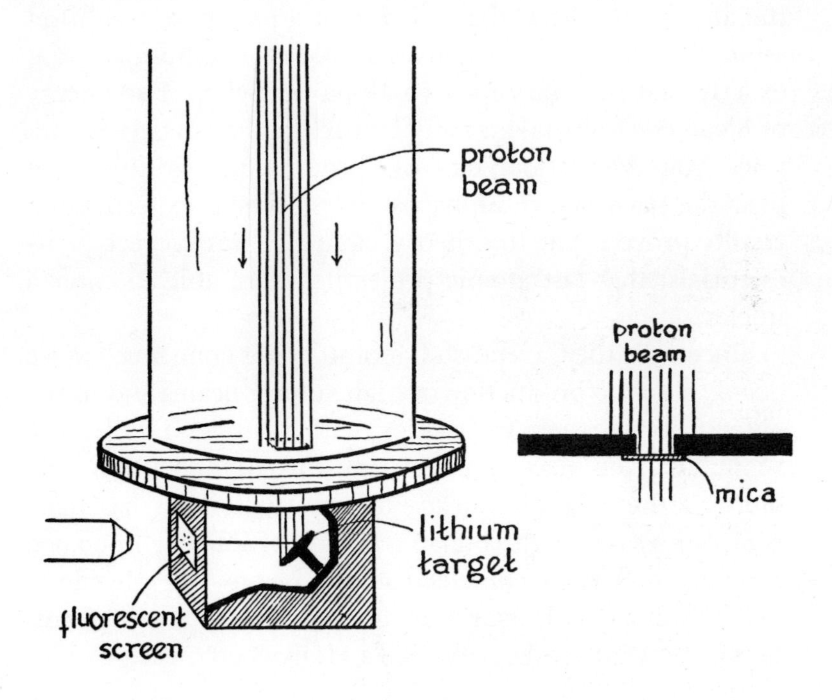

reactions. A fluorescent screen and microscope were set up at right angles to the beam, with the metal target arranged at an angle of 45° facing both the screen and the beam. When the target was made of lithium metal, scintillations were immediately observed on the screen. The range of protons scattered from the plate was too short to produce these scintillations. Consequently the effect was due to particles originating in the plate itself, particles which disappeared when the proton beam was interrupted. This was definite proof that the protons had disintegrated lithium.

In their first report, dated April 16, 1932, Cockcroft and Walton cautiously put forward their results thus, "It seems not unlikely that the lithium isotope of mass 7 occasionally captures a proton and the resulting nucleus of mass 8 breaks into two alpha particles, each of mass 4 and each with an energy of about eight million electron volts." Further confirmation for this hypothesis is provided by consideration of the atomic numbers; the addition of a proton to a lithium atom of atomic number 3 gives a total atomic number of 4, exactly that necessary for two alpha particles. The energy of 8,000,000 volts taken away by each alpha particle is supplied from the excess in mass of a proton plus a lithium atom over the mass of two alpha particles. These experimental results proved that the theory of nuclei was correct in its essentials; that fast atomic projectiles were able to enter a nucleus.

Since 1932 the Cavendish Laboratory has gone much more deeply into the production of high voltage beams and in the observation of their interaction with matter. The lecture room has given place to a new beautiful High Tension Laboratory; the original Cockcroft and Walton set has been replaced by two high voltage sets, one producing 1,000,000 and the other 2,000,000 electron volt beams. The inside of the laboratory with its tremendous spaces and rounded corners to prevent sparks looks like a Hollywood director's idea

Reproduced by permission from "The Newer Alchemy," by Lord Rutherford: Cambridge University Press; The Macmillan Company

The Cockcroft and Walton original voltage doubler at the Cavendish. The tube at the right is the accelerating tube; the glass one at the left contains the rectifiers. Cockcroft in the background.

A. K. Solomon

Professor J. D. Cockcroft watching a Cavendish laboratory cricket match about 1938.

The 2,000,000 volt generator now at the Cavendish laboratory. The tall tower on the right contai the rectifiers and condensers. The rectifiers are clearly visible as the diagonals connecting th two towers. The complex of shorter towers on the left contains the accelerating tube, the vol meter, and the belt for running the discharge. The business end of the accelerating tube is in research room directly below the standing man.

of the world of tomorrow. For safety the sets were dismantled and were stored under the concrete floor of the laboratory for the duration. As originally pointed out, the advantage of an atom smasher of this type is that it provides a large continuous current of particles at a voltage that itself stays constant. The early experiments on transmutation with naturally produced alpha particles had relied on a weapon already supplied. But in the Cockcroft and Walton experiments the weapon was itself hand-forged from protons and electricity. This was artificial transmutation in its purest sense.

CHAPTER 9

ATOM SMASHERS 2 – VAN DE GRAAFF GENERATOR

Before Cockcroft and Walton's brilliant results appeared, two men were at work in America on high voltage generators that were to provide added opportunity for nuclear research. One of these, Robert Van de Graaff, one time Rhodes scholar, in 1931 developed at Princeton the electrostatic generator which bears his name. According to Van de Graaff, the idea was originally conceived by Lord Kelvin, the famous nineteenth-century physicist who contributed so much to our knowledge of heat and electricity. Various other scientists discussed the general possibilities of the idea in the intervening years, but it was not until Van de Graaff built his machine at Princeton that the idea was developed practically.

The first electrostatic generator produced only 80,000 volts; a later 1,500,000 model was small enough to be exhibited on a lecture table to an admiring freshman physics class at Princeton. The high point of the demonstration came when Van de Graaff's hair stood on end – proof positive that high voltage had been generated. The demonstration was important because the action of the generator depended on a principle supposedly familiar to the freshman class. It is possible to spray electric charge on to a moving belt and later to remove that charge from the belt at some further point in its travel. The process is just as simple as getting on an escalator at one floor and getting off at the next. In Van de Graaff's generator the ground floor was the earth or the lecture desk, and the top floor was a smooth surfaced conducting sphere supported by an insulating column. On the ground floor a motor drove a belt made of silk or some other insulating material over a pulley inside the top sphere. A set of charged points, often victrola needles, arranged like a metallic comb sprayed charge from a small, low voltage generator on to the belt down at the bottom. At the top another set of points connected by a wire to the sphere collected the charge from the belt. In this man-

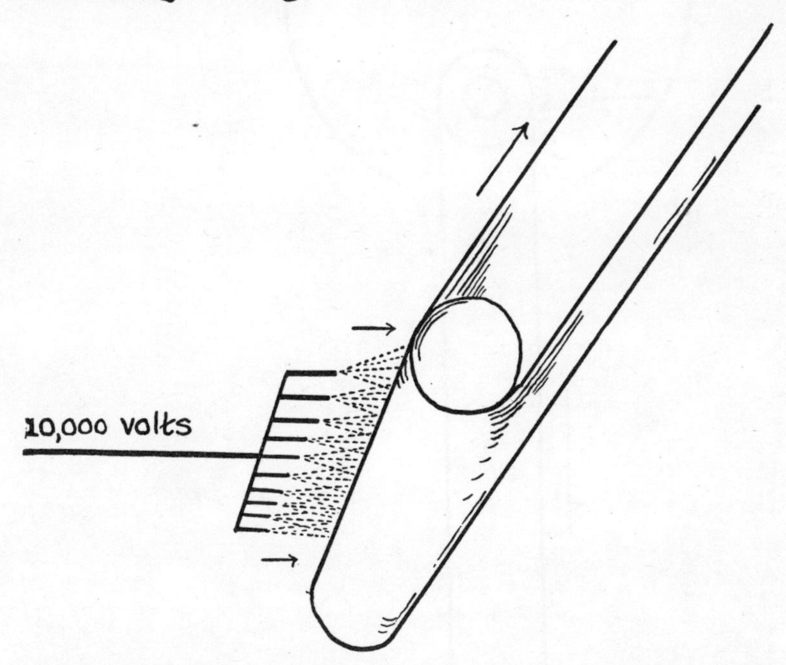

ner charge could be ferried up continually until the sphere attained the desired voltage. The voltage which it would reach depended not only on the position of the sphere relative to other objects, but also on the rate at which the charge was brought up to it, less the rate at which charge leaked away. The number of people on the second floor of a department store is exactly the number of people who have come to the floor less the number who have left it.

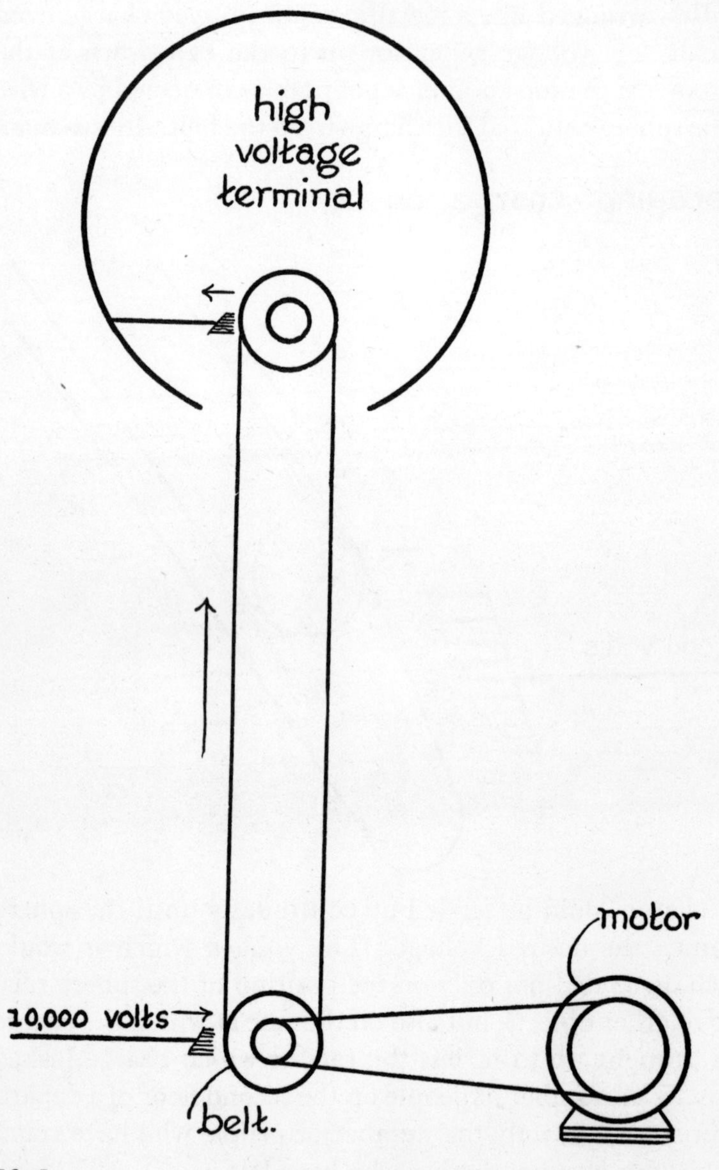
Van de Graaff — electrostatic generator
high
voltage
terminal
motor
10,000 volts
belt.

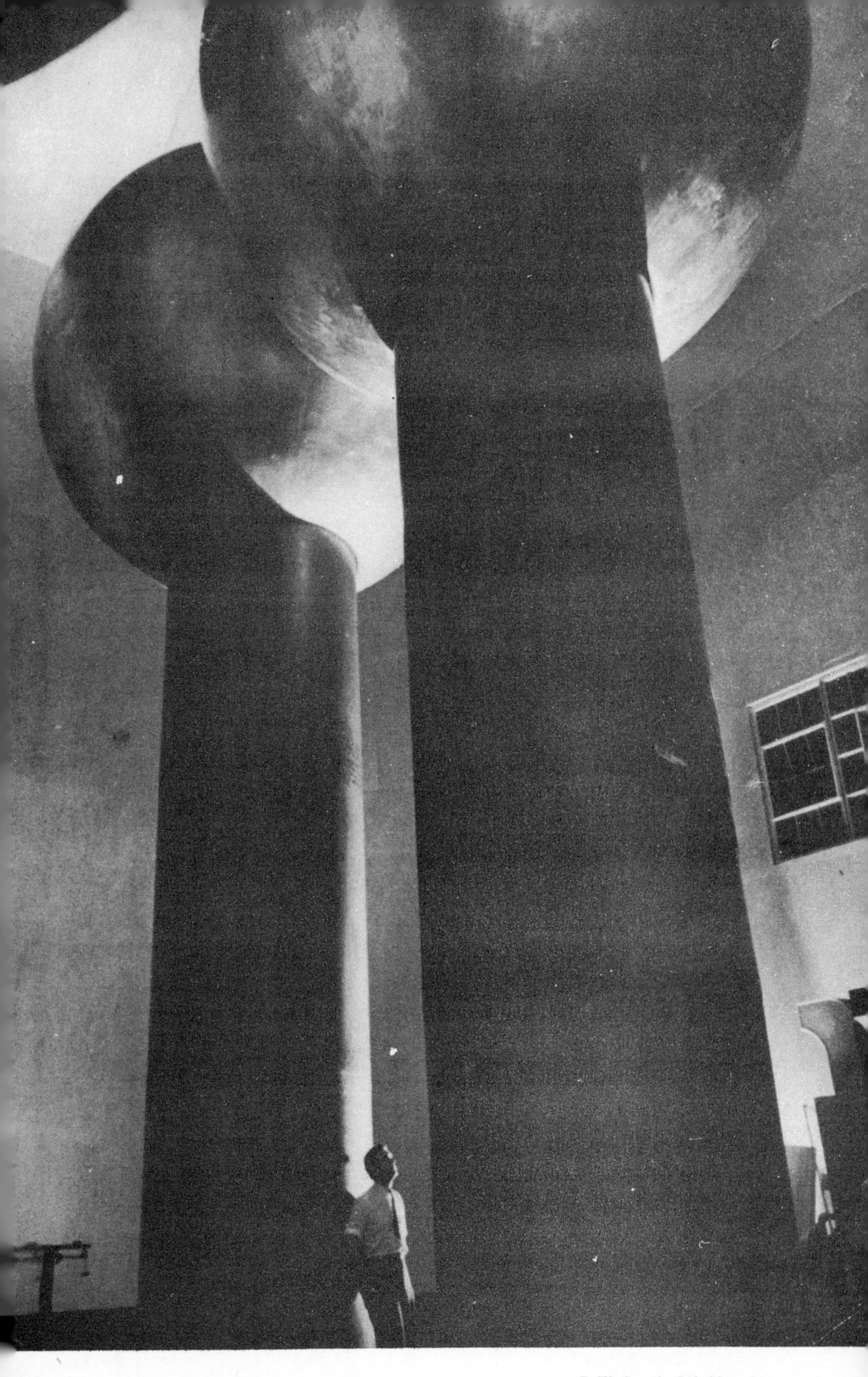

F. W. Goro for Life Magazine

The Van de Graaff generator now at Massachusetts Institute of Technology.

Reproduced by courtesy of the Massachusetts Institute of Technology

The 5,000,000 volt Van de Graaff generator sparking to the hangar walls. This generator has now been moved to a new building at M. I. T.

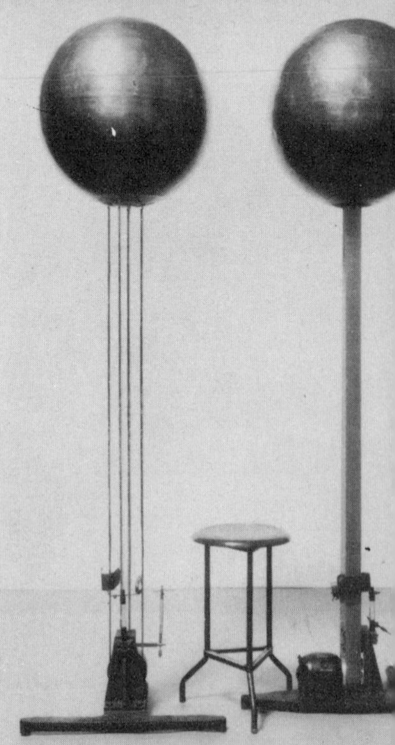

W. Clayton

The small 1,500,000 volt Van de Graaff generator built at Princeton.

The simple principle on which the operation of the electrostatic generator depends is that although a closed conducting sphere is charged to a high voltage, there are no electrical forces inside it. However intense the field due to the high voltage may be outside the sphere, there is no field inside. If the sphere is opened and a single charge brought in, there will be an electric field due to that charge, but once the charge has touched the sphere the field will disappear. In an electrostatic generator there is a small field inside the sphere due to those charges which have entered and have not yet been collected. As they are collected the field would disappear, were not this loss compensated by new charges brought into the sphere on the belt. When the charged belt has entered the sphere it has no difficulty giving up its charge, for it is in a region almost free of electrical field. The sphere will continue to accept charge regardless of its own voltage, that is, regardless of the electric field outside it. Once the fairy tale hero has penetrated the ring of fire round the magic mountain he is free to woo the heroine in her castle on the mountain top. In an electrostatic generator there is a danger that the fire may become real, that is, that the sphere may spark to neighboring objects outside and so discharge itself. Another great difficulty is the belt, for it must not only be flexible enough to pass easily over the pulleys top and bottom, but also so good an insulator that the sphere will not use the belt as a path for sparks to ground.

The results with the first small generator, as well as with the 1,500,000 volt one built at a cost of less than one hundred dollars were so encouraging that work was begun by Van de Graaff and others at Massachusetts Institute of Technology on a really large electrostatic generator. The Institute was especially fortunate in obtaining the use of a dirigible hangar at Round Hill not far from Boston in which to construct the new gigantic machine. The New Haven Railroad kindly donated almost a quarter mile of tracks so that the generator, mounted on a truck, could be moved out of the hangar into the air to test its action under various atmospheric conditions. The spheres themselves, towering 43 feet above the ground, were 15 feet in diameter, so large that it was possible to construct a laboratory inside them. If it was safe for the electric charge inside, then it was safe for the hero.

The large generator made use of several improvements already devised for the smaller ones. The belt not only brought positive charge up to the sphere, but also removed negative charge on the downward journey, thus doubling its efficiency. With the construction of a second electrostatic generator to be charged negatively the voltage difference was doubled. When one generator was charged positively to 1,000,000 volts, and the other negatively to the same amount, the voltage across them was 2,000,000 volts, just twice that between either one and ground. Housing the belt inside the hollow supporting column for the charged sphere offered still another improvement. At Round Hill this was especially necessary, for near the sea the humidity was so high that the insulation difficulties were at first almost insurmountable; though dry air is a good insulator, damp air is a very poor one. To keep the humidity at a reasonable level a complete air conditioning system was installed inside the column. Inclusion of laboratory space within the sphere added certain requirements not present in the smaller machines. To reduce the vibration caused by the motors in the truck below, they were mounted on rubber supports just as automobile motors are mounted to keep from transmitting the vibration to the car body. Only then could sensitive measuring instruments be used inside the sphere. As in the Cockcroft and Walton generator, power supplies were needed not only to run the discharge tube and accessory apparatus, but also to provide light for the laboratory. In this case, as with Cockcroft and Walton, a belt transmitted power from a motor on the truck below to a generator in the laboratory above. Heat was supplied by the air conditioning system. Finally in March of 1936, Van de Graaff and his collaborators announced that the new generator could produce 5,000,000 volts.

Application of this generator to nuclear research required the construction of a tube for accelerating the particles; the difficulties encountered in its construction were so great that it was never completed. Furthermore the laboratories inside the sphere could not be used during operation, because the neutron radiation was too intense. In view of these difficulties, the two generator towers have been joined together and are now used to produce a beam of 2,500,000 volt particles that is directed downwards against targets safely placed underground.

Smaller generators are more practical for nuclear research. Accelerating tubes can be made to function at lower voltages. The huge size of the 5,000,000 volt generator limits its availability to research laboratories which already have, or are able to construct, buildings large enough to house it. As the voltage desired increases, the size of the generator increases tremendously. Besides, the difficulties met in construction and operation become much greater as the voltage is pushed higher. A small Van de Graaff generator has been in constant use in Washington for several years. And at Harvard one only eight and a half feet high is now in operation producing 600,000 volt deuterons. Even the last World's Fair in Paris boasted a Van de Graaff generator.

However, it is possible to reach high voltage, even while limiting the size, using a method suggested in the original article by Van de Graaff and his collaborators. Building the generator in a better insulating medium than ordinary air obviates many of the difficulties of discharge to surrounding objects which made necessary the huge size of the Round Hill machine. Before beginning construction on the giant, a smaller generator had been proposed for operation in a vacuum, but the difficulties encountered during construction led to temporary abandonment in favor of work on the 5,000,000 volt generator. At Wisconsin University the problem was attacked from another angle, also suggested by the original collaborators. Air at high pressure, while not so efficient an insulator as vacuum, was a far better one than normal air. Constructed to work at eight times normal atmospheric pressure, the Wisconsin generator produced almost 2,500,000 volts within a restricted space.

The development of a pressure generator, like the development of all research apparatus, was not without its problems and troubles. A shell strong enough to withstand the pressure and large enough to hold the generator was required. The hazard of fire made exceptionally stringent precautions necessary. Fire requires oxygen; in the presence of compressed air many things become readily inflammable which would only smolder and extinguish themselves under normal conditions. At Wisconsin, there were four fires, mostly caused by apparently uninflammable material that burned in the oxygen rich atmosphere. Freon gas, manufactured especially for use in refrigerating systems, a gas which is not only non-inflammable but also has exceptional electrical insulating properties, has been successfully substituted for compressed air.

With these developments, sometimes used together, sometimes used only in part, the Van de Graaff generator has become a reliable source of high voltage particles. Like the voltage doubler, these generators produce a continuous stream of particles all accelerated to a stable and known voltage, and are used extensively in this country for nuclear research.

There remains another demonstration of the importance of these generators. As it is possible to accelerate positively charged particles, so is it possible to accelerate negative par-

F. W. Goro for Life Magazine

...ing up the pressure Van de Graaff ...rator at the Westinghouse Re-...h Laboratories. The white belt ...e left carries the charge up to the ... In the center can be seen the ... vacuum accelerating tube.

F. W. Goro for Life Magazine

Robert Van de Graaff.

F. W. Goro for Life Magazine

Four million volt pressure Van de Graaff generator built by the Westinghouse Research Laboratories at East Pittsburgh, Pa.

ticles in an electrostatic generator which develops voltage of opposite sign. Electrons have been accelerated in Van de Graaff generators to energies of over 1,000,000 electron volts. Such electrons can be used as projectiles in x-ray tubes, producing 1,000,000 volt x-rays, a radiation especially valuable in the treatment of malignant diseases. A 1,000,000 volt x-ray tube has already been completed and construction is now under way on a 3,000,000 volt pressure tube to be used in hospitals. It is important to note that these developments have arisen out of fundamental research in physical problems, not as a result of a direct effort to construct x-ray tubes. This is but a single example of close collaboration between physics and medicine on an important technical advance which has arisen as a by-product of research on the nature of matter.

CHAPTER 10

ATOM SMASHERS 3 – THE CYCLOTRON

IN 1929, even before Cockcroft and Walton reported their preliminary work on acceleration of particles, Ernest Lawrence a young physicist at the University of California began experiments that were to lead to the development of the cyclotron. The cyclotron is the atom smasher that, more than any other, has demonstrated the international character of physics. Cyclotrons are completed or a-building in Tokyo, Leningrad, Stockholm, Copenhagen, Paris, and in England, in Liverpool, Birmingham, and Cambridge, and many more are scattered throughout the United States. Lawrence himself has been awarded the Nobel prize for their development. The voltage doubler and the Van de Graaff generator deliver their voltage in one big dose; Lawrence and his collaborators decided to use repeated application of a much lower voltage. With a lower voltage, many of the problems of insulation against sparks that had played such a prominent part in the development of other atom smashers were eliminated.

Particles entering one end of a long glass tube were accelerated by passage through a number of cylindrical electrodes. Once inside the electrodes, as in the Van de Graaff spheres, the particles were in field free space. They could be accelerated only by the electric fields between the electrodes; change of voltage on an electrode could not affect a particle once it was safely inside. A single voltage of, say, 20,000 volts could be applied repeatedly to accelerate the particles to 200,000 volts, with the sole requirement that the voltage between two successive electrodes be 20,000 at the moment the particle passed from one to the other. When the particle emerged from the first electrode, it was attracted toward the second by the voltage between them. Then, once inside the second, conditions were rapidly changed, and the voltage applied between the second and third electrodes. The particle was accelerated again in the strong field between these two electrodes and the process repeated with enough successive electrodes so that the particle finally attained the required energy of 200,000 electron volts. The problem was to keep the voltage always in step with the

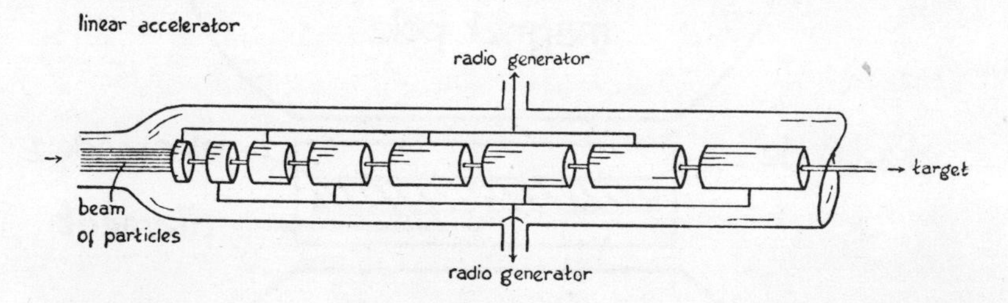

particle, so that as it reached each separate electrode, the volts were there as well to pull the particle along. Lawrence used a short wave radio generator to provide a rapidly changing voltage and finally, in 1931, he announced the production of 1,250,000 electron volt particles.

The difficulty with such a method is the length of the tube. The possibilities of radio set a limit to the voltage on each electrode, and once this limit is reached higher energy can be secured only by making the tube longer. Even then, as the energy of the particles increases, they are more difficult to handle and the internal structure of the tube must become more complex. It has been said that Lawrence's unique solution of this problem was suggested by an obscure paper on the action of these particles in magnetic fields. The solution is as simple as it is ingenious. In a strong magnetic field charged particles travel in circular orbits; their path can be adjusted so that they circulate inside two large electrodes. As in the linear accelerator an oscillating voltage is applied to these electrodes and the particles are accelerated each time they leave one electrode and enter the other. A vacuum tight metal box containing the two electrodes is placed between the poles of a magnet, and at one stroke all

Lawrence — cyclotron

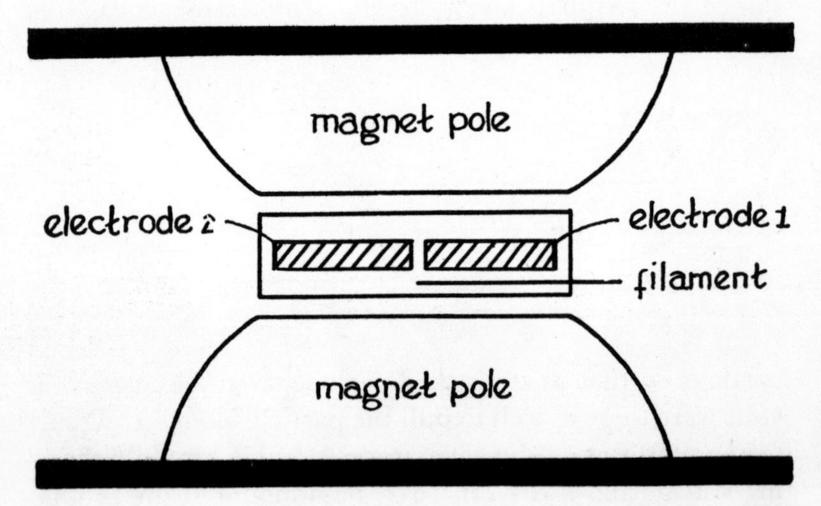

the cumbersome glass tubing becomes unnecessary. With the abolition of the glass tubing comes the abolition of the accelerating tube, the feature that caused so much trouble with other high voltage machines.

The trajectory of the particles is shown in the spiral line in the figure. As the particle gains voltage it goes faster, and the faster it goes the more difficult it is for the magnet to force it into a circular path. As a result, the particle describes circles of larger and larger radius. A peculiar and important law applying to particles in a uniform magnetic field states that, regardless of velocity, like particles will describe a semicircle in exactly the same time. Thus it takes as long for the projectiles to get from A to B as from B to C, or C to E and so on. Although they have increasingly large

modern linear accelerator developed Cornell University. The target is at ıe top right – the end of the glass enclosed accelerating tube.

From an exhibit in the Science Museum, South Kensington, London. Reproduced by permission of Professor E. O. Lawrence

An early twelve inch cyclotron which used only one dee.

P. Donaldson

The Harvard cyclotron tank with its top cover removed. The two dees can be seen clearly. The deflector at the upper left pulls the ions into the target chamber at the upper right. The dee supports can be seen in the left foreground. The water-cooled plate above the center of the dees is not the filament; it is a collector to keep the filament beam from bombarding the top of the cyclotron tank.

distances to travel, the particles are going increasingly fast, and the increase in speed exactly makes up for the increase in path.

The first cyclotron, only 4 inches across, could easily be placed between the poles of a small magnet. The results were so encouraging that Lawrence proceeded to build his

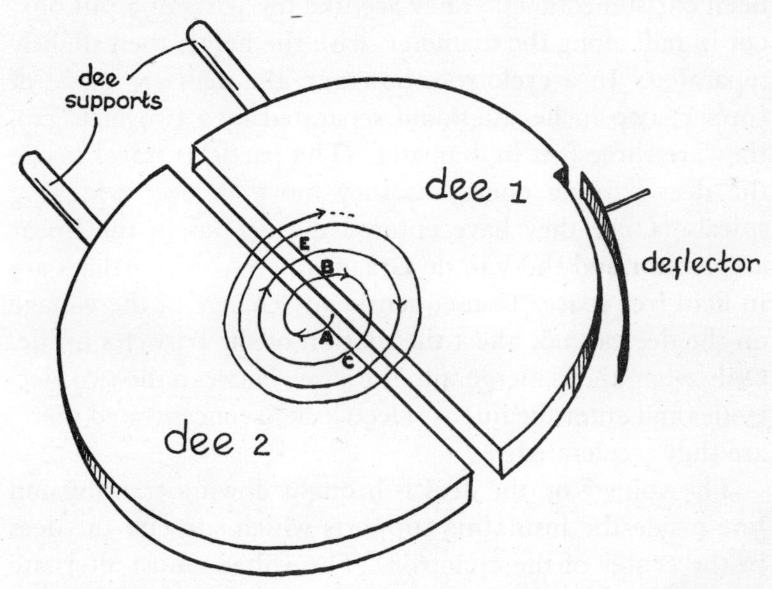

12 inch cyclotron, now on exhibition in the Science Museum in London. To construct an even larger cyclotron the first necessity was a magnet, and Lawrence was especially fortunate in the gift of an 85 ton magnet, large enough to take a 37 inch cyclotron between the poles. This machine, now in operation, produces deuterons with energies of about 8,000,000 volts. Yet the demands of modern science far exceed the supply, so the cyclotron is run continuously 24 hours a day. At the Cavendish Laboratory, in the room once occupied by Cockcroft and Walton's voltage doubler, we have constructed a 36 inch cyclotron which produces 9,000,000 volt deuterons. Meanwhile in California, still unsatisfied, Lawrence and his collaborators have already com-

pleted a 60 inch cyclotron. The emergent deuterons from this cyclotron with its 220 ton magnet have an energy of 16,000,000 volts, far higher than ever attained by laboratory methods before.

From above, each of the two hollow semi-cylindrical electrodes in the cyclotron looks like the letter "D," so they have been christened dees. They are like the parts of a pill box, cut in half along the diameter, with the halves then slightly separated. In a cyclotron, however, the dees are made of copper; two inches high and separated by a two inch gap, they are three feet in diameter. The particles travel inside the dees gaining energy as they move in ever widening spirals. Once they have entered the dee, as in the linear accelerator and the Van de Graaff spheres, the particles are in field free space. Consequently any change of the voltage on the dee can not affect the motion of the particles inside. Only when they emerge into the space between the two electrodes and enter the intense electric field concentrated there, are they accelerated.

The voltage on the dees is brought down a transmission line inside the insulating supports which suspend the dees in the center of the cyclotron. The voltage must alternate rapidly from dee to dee. That is, a particle at A must be attracted into dee number 2; then, when the same particle gets to B, it must be attracted again into dee number 1. So while the particle is traveling in the field free space from A to B the voltage must change from dee number 2 to dee number 1. Then as the particle goes on from B to C the volts must return to dee number 2, and so on. In the Cavendish cyclotron, the voltage makes a complete change from dee to dee 12,000,000 times a second. The only method known for producing this rapid change is modern radio technique. Twelve million times a second represents a frequency of 12 megacycles, or a wave length of 25 meters — a wave length in the range used for foreign broadcasting.

Consequently the cyclotron builder is forced to construct a transmitter, whose power requirements would stagger an ordinary amateur. For example, the Cavendish cyclotron is powered by somewhat more than 100 kilowatts. In comparison, most powerful short-wave transmitters operating on about the same wave length are rated at from 10 to 50 kilowatts. In radio the effort is to broadcast the power; in the cyclotron the difficulty is to keep it in and make it all, or a large portion of it, appear on the dees. The Cavendish cyclotron has been built in the midst of a group of other laboratories; the loud and voluble complaints of other scientists have impelled every possible effort to keep the wireless waves from getting out of the room and disturbing their instruments.

A larger pill box provides the body of the cyclotron, which is the tank. This pill box is made of brass, with heavy steel for its top and bottom, because the steel enhances the action of the magnet and makes the magnetic field stronger inside the box. The tank is so heavy that a crane is needed to lift the top off when the cyclotron is moved out from between the poles of the magnet for inspection or repair. The walls of the tank are pierced with holes through which enter the supports for the dees and the other accessory apparatus required inside the tank. Furthermore, for the particles to whirl round satisfactorily inside the tank, a vacuum is necessary, since, if the pressure is too high the particles collide with others they meet in their travel. Such a collision deflects the particle from its normal path, and it wanders about haphazardly inside the tank until it hits a wall or loses its energy in some other way. It is comparatively easy to pump all the air out of a small 6 inch cyclotron and keep it out, but when the cyclotron has grown to a 3 foot one, the task becomes very difficult. The heavy steel top of the cyclotron is clamped down on a rubber gasket so tightly that no air can creep in, and all the other removable joints around the wall of the cyclotron are also sealed by rubber gaskets. Even with the most careful precautions, the cyclotron tank sometimes springs a leak: then operations must be suspended until the leak is found and repaired.

The particles to be accelerated in the cyclotron are formed at the very center of the tank. A hot filament rests in a case on the floor of the tank, between the dees. The electrons emitted by the filament receive an initial acceleration in an electric field which can be applied between the filament and

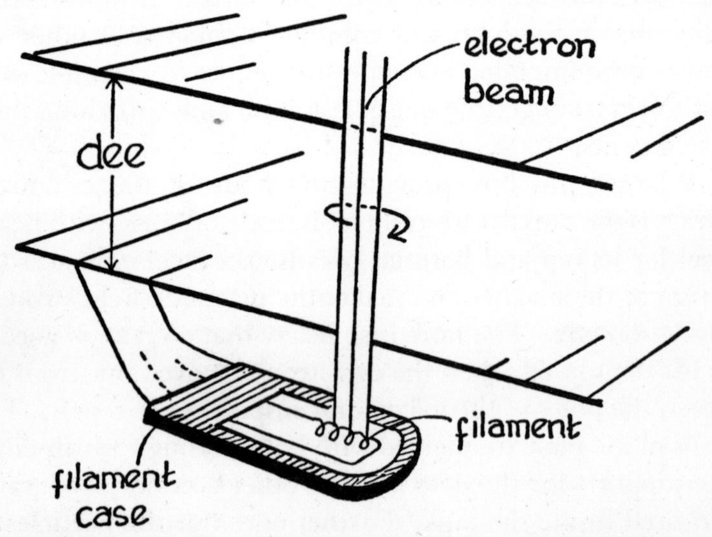

the case. With this start they speed to the top of the tank; in the magnetic field the electron path is curled into tight little spirals – much smaller than those of the deuterons because the electrons are so much lighter. These spirals are so small that they can not be seen; the electron beam appears as a sharply defined blue shaft stretching from the bottom to the top of the tank between the dees. The deuterons are formed by the action of this beam on heavy hydrogen gas admitted into the tank in minute quantities through an adjustable gas valve. When an electron in the beam hits a heavy hydrogen gas atom, it may strip off the loosely bound external electron, leaving behind a positively charged heavy hydrogen nucleus, a deuteron. Some of the deuterons formed at A are attracted into dee number 2, and set out on their long spiral journey inside the tank.

The cyclotron beam must be focussed to be effective. Otherwise the particles would spread out vertically, hit the top or bottom of the dee and lose all their energy. When it emerges, the beam must be directed at a small target, rather than scattered at random over a large area. The shotgun is not very useful in scoring bull's-eyes. The electric field that exists between the dees, as well as the natural action of the magnetic field, acts to focus the beam. In the center of the tank, the field between the dees tends to keep the beam narrow and well focussed as it passes from dee to dee. But as the beam gets farther out towards the periphery of the dees, the particles are traveling so fast as they go through the electric field, that the focussing effect becomes less important. It is fortunate that here the magnetic focussing begins to come into action and tends to keep the particles from diverging.

Matching these two effects so that the final beam is neither too wide nor too narrow is a difficult task. "Shims," iron sheets inserted between the magnet poles and the cyclotron tank, are used for the final adjustments. The position of these shims is highly critical, and makes a great difference in the number of particles which finally arrive at the target after their passage of almost 60 yards from the center of the tank. In Lawrence's early cyclotrons the target itself was inside the tank. Nonetheless, it was necessary to pull the particles away from their normal trajectory to the target beyond the dee. This was accomplished by application of a negative voltage to a subsidiary electrode, the deflector, which drew the positively charged nuclei through a window in the dee and directed them towards the target. But the deflector could not always pull all the particles through; many of them hit the dee near the window and were lost from the beam. The heat generated by these impacts was very great because the particles had acquired their maximum energy by the time they reached the window. Consequently, a thin plate made of molybdenum, a tough heat resistant metal, was substituted for the copper of the dee just where the particles hit.

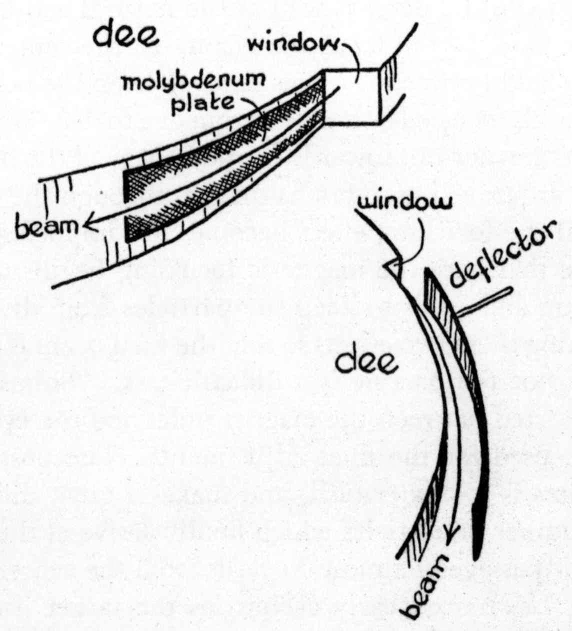

As cyclotrons grew in size and usefulness it became desirable to have the target outside the tank so that it would be readily available. With a target chamber welded onto the tank wall, it was easy to fashion a vacuum gate which would shut the target chamber off from the main vacuum inside the tank when targets were changed. This is a very important feature because it makes it possible to bombard many different targets in rapid succession without loss of the

P. Donaldson

The Harvard cyclotron deflector assembly, showing the window in the dee, the deflector and the entrance to the target chamber.

Press Association, Inc.

Professor Ernest Lawrence at the controls of the University of California cyclotron.

The new 60 inch cyclotron at the University of California.

D. Cooksey

precious main vacuum. To deflect the particles to an external target so far from their natural orbit requires a large voltage on the deflector, sometimes as high as 60,000 to 100,000 volts. However, the disadvantage and difficulties of keeping so high a voltage on the deflector are far outweighed by the advantage of an easily accessible target.

In the early days of work with x-rays and radium, many workers were very badly burned because they were not aware of the effects of lasting exposure to the rays. A similar problem exists with the cyclotron which produces neutrons in very large quantities from bombardment of the copper dees by deuterons lost from the main beam. For safety the cyclotron is completely surrounded by water tanks 3 feet thick – a veritable wall of water. And if this should not suffice, the control table, from which the machine is operated, can be removed into a neighbouring room. As yet there have been no reports of any lasting harm coming to cyclotron workers as a result of overexposure.

Although the cyclotron embodies a very simple and ingenious principle, it is not easy to construct. At the Cavendish the first plans were drawn up in October 1936, and laboratory construction began a year later. From October 1937 until September 1939 at least three scientists were constantly at work. Yet only in the spring of 1939 did the cyclotron produce a peak beam of 14 microamperes of 9,000,000 volt deuterons, a power output of 126 watts. About 120,000 watts are required to run the magnet and the wireless station to produce these 126 watts of 9,000,000 volt deuterons. The Harvard cyclotron, on the other hand, yields a steady beam of up to 50 microamperes at 11,000,000 volts with only 70,000 watts input. And in California the 8,000,000 volt cyclotron runs with a beam as high as 100 microamperes at higher power input.

The cyclotron does not serve for the production of a steady current at a constant and known voltage as do the voltage doubler and the Van de Graaff generator. The current is not steady since the cyclotron adjustments are so critical, and the voltage may have a spread of as much as 1,000,000 volts since all of the particles do not start exactly in the center. On the other hand, the voltage available from the cyclotron is far higher than that available from any other source for nuclear research. The disintegration of elements depends on voltage to so great an extent that when deuterons bombard platinum an increase of voltage from 5,500,000 to 8,000,000 electron volts will increase the number of disintegrations one hundred fold. The same is true of the yields of many other nuclear reactions. Consequently, the cyclotron is the most powerful weapon available today for nuclear disintegration.

The operation of so powerful a machine has been described far more concisely. One day a very elderly lady came to see the machine. She took one horrified look at the room, with its complexity of apparatus and diagram. Then before I could say a word, "Thank you very much, young man. I see what you do. You lead the atom around until it is so dizzy it breaks up in despair." And so we do.

P. Donaldson

Broadside view of a horizontal beam (parallel to wooden magnet cover) of 11,000,000 volt deuterons emerging into the air from the Harvard cyclotron.

P. Donal

A modern Geiger counter, showing the mechanical recorder and an electrical scaling circuit which cords only one out of every sixteen particles entering the tube, thus permitting high counting spe

A modern Geiger tube with an outside brass electrode whose wall is only 4/1000th of an inch th

P. Donal

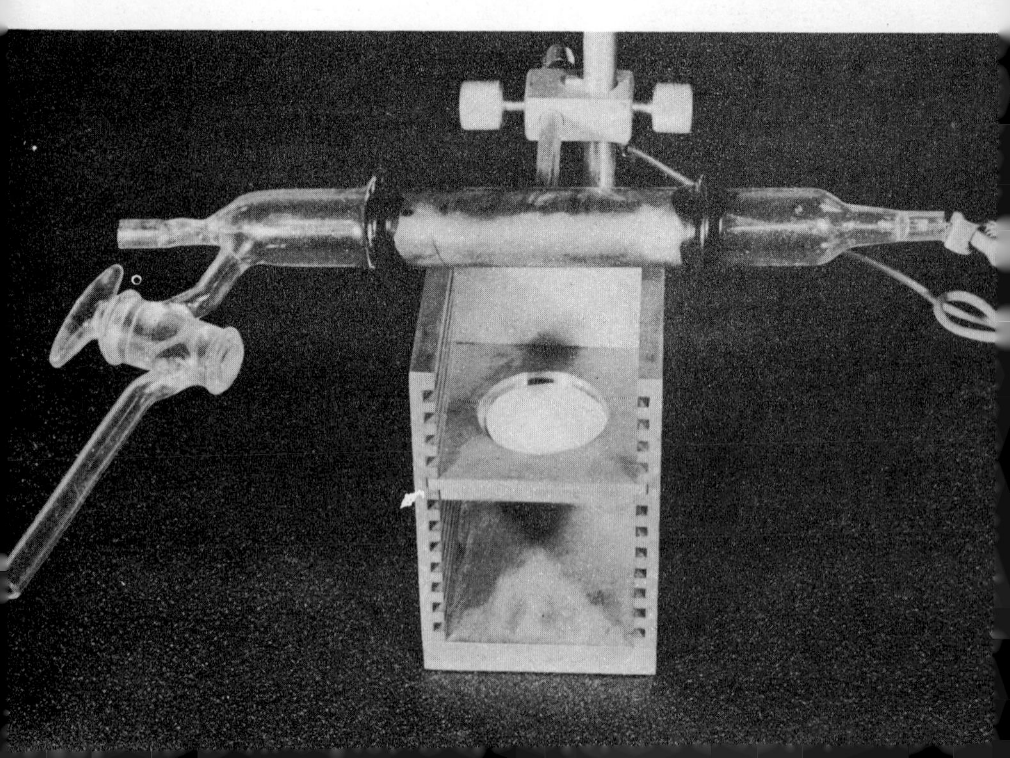

CHAPTER 11

THE GEIGER COUNTER

To find out what is inside the atom, to learn what makes the atom tick, it is necessary not only to be able to take the atom apart, but also to recognize the parts that have come off. This is a problem that existed even before artificial transmutation was discovered; it is a problem whose solution was necessary to unravel the mystery of natural radioactivity. Fortunately, charged particles, like alpha and beta particles, produce an electrical effect when they pass through matter. When an alpha particle passes close to another atom – not to another nucleus but to the outside of any atom – it is very likely to knock an outside electron off the atom. Sometimes the electron is removed because of direct collision with the bombarding nucleus, a billiard ball effect; but far oftener it is pulled off in the wake of the particle, much as a flowing cape knocks an article off a table all unnoticed. The wind of the passing particle seems to have sucked the electron off the neutral atom. The attraction, which works for beta particles and gamma rays as well, is electrical. It takes a certain amount of work to remove an electron, however loosely bound, from an atom, so each time the process occurs the passing particle gives up a little of its energy.

Each encounter takes only a little of the impinging particle's energy, but the process is cumulative; electrical interaction with the matter it travels through brings the particle to a final stop. The alpha particle, with its great mass and double charge, reacts most strongly with electrons. In fact, an alpha particle traveling initially with a velocity of 45,000,000 miles an hour knocks so many electrons off neutral atoms that it is brought to a dead stop in 3.3 inches. The light beta particle with its single charge has a much less intense effect, and the non-corpuscular gamma ray even less than the beta particle. The less intense the effect, the further the particle can travel; it is therefore to be expected that the beta ray will be more penetrating than the alpha, and the gamma even more than the beta.

When an electron has been removed from a neutral atom, it does not follow in the track of the alpha particle. Rather, a nearby neutral atom usually captures it. The first atom, the donor of the electron, becomes positively charged once it has lost the negative charge of the electron. On the other hand, the capturing atom receives an extra negative charge. Consequently, after the whirlwind passage of the alpha particle two neutral atoms are changed to two charged atoms, called ions, one positive, and one negative. The ejection of the electron is called ionisation; the two atoms

ionisation

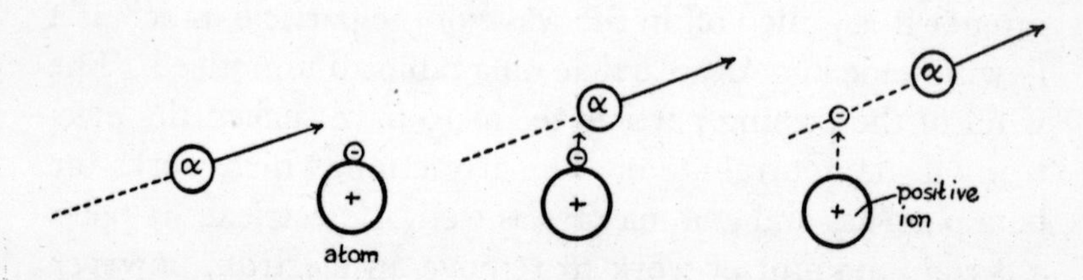

participating in the ejection and subsequent capture become an ion pair.

The ions are collected in an ionisation chamber so that passage of the particle may be detected by measurement of its ionisation. The chamber consists of two parallel flat electrodes in an air filled box. Ordinary dry air is a reasonably good insulator as is shown by experience with the Van de Graaff generator. Consequently, when an electric field is applied to the electrodes, there is only a very slight current flow. As soon as a beam of alpha particles enters the chamber through a thin window, the air molecules inside become ionised. If the field between the plates is small the ions drift about and finally recombine: the gas returns to its normal non-conducting state. On the other hand, if the electric field is intense, the ions are attracted to the electrodes and separate before they have the opportunity to recombine.

ionisation chamber

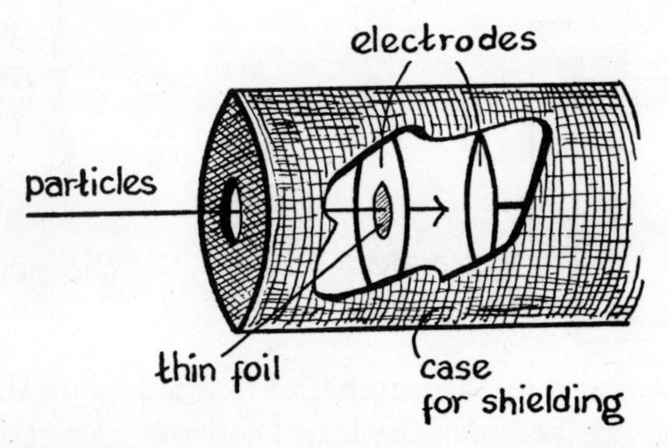

All the ions of one sign hasten to one of the electrodes; measurement of the charge brought by the ions gives accurately the amount of ionisation produced by the alpha particle beam.

The electroscope, an instrument even simpler than the ionisation chamber, can also measure alpha radiation. In its simplest form an electroscope consists merely of two thin gold leaves enclosed in an airtight box. The gold leaves are hung on a metal support from which a single insulated wire is brought out from the box. When the metal support is charged, say positively, the leaves will fly apart; since each possesses a charge of the same sign they repel each other. If the gas in the box is non-conducting, and if the system is well insulated, the leaves will retain their charge as well as their position for some time. As soon as radiation produces any ionisation in the chamber, the negative ions are attracted to the leaves, where giving up their own charge they neutralize that on the leaves. The leaves, now no longer charged, slowly collapse together. The intensity of the

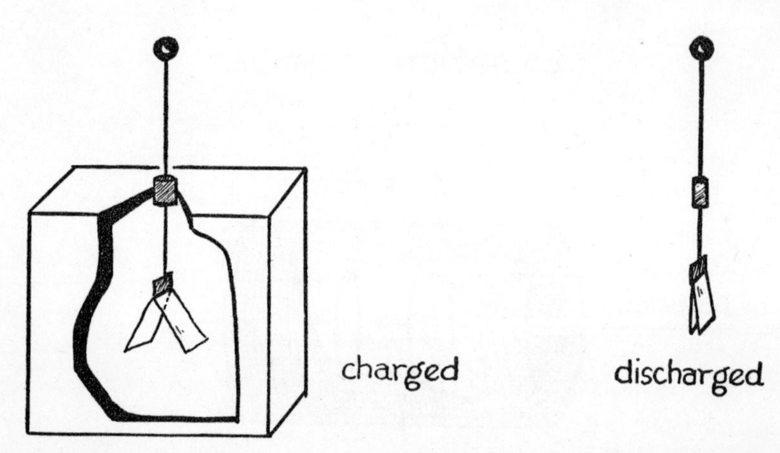

ionisation is measured by the number of ions falling on the leaf, that is, the rate at which the leaves collapse. An early improvement in the electroscope was the substitution of a stationary plate for one of the gold leaves; subsequently, the electroscope was tilted at an angle to obtain even greater sensitivity. A modern electroscope uses in place of the gold leaf a tiny metal-coated quartz fiber, the movement of which is observed through a microscope. This electroscope possesses the advantages of small size and high sensitivity combined with especial ruggedness; consequently, instruments of this type are much in demand for measurements today.

In early experiments with radioactivity the ionisation chamber was connected directly to the sensitive measuring instrument. At that time there were no instruments delicate enough to record the ionisation produced by the passage of a single alpha particle through the chamber. Though accurate, the motion of the pointer over the scale in the most sensitive instruments was so sluggish that, even if measurable, only a few particles could be counted per minute. The invention of the string electrometer in which sudden displacements of a quartz fiber were observed through a microscope first gave a method of making many observations in a short period. The fiber returned to its normal position almost instantaneously and its motion was recorded by photography on moving film. But even the string electrometer could not record single alpha particles. After the invention of radio, linear amplifiers were devised which could multiply the ionisation current from a single alpha particle to a value which would register on an electrometer. Today the final ionisation current is often shown visibly on the screen of an oscilloscope, an apparatus which employs a television tube with a moving beam of electrons as scale and pointer. The beam normally travels rapidly back and forth along a single line across the screen. When a particle is recorded the beam momentarily kicks sharply upward showing a jagged peak on the screen. The height of the peak is proportional to the amplified ionisation current of the particle.

But in 1908 these refinements were unknown. At that time Rutherford was especially anxious to find the charge carried by a single alpha particle, as well as the number of alpha particles given off in one second by a gram of radium. He had already obtained a value for the total charge of the particles given off by a gram of radium per second, but this could not be translated directly into terms of the number of particles without knowing whether the alpha particle was singly or doubly charged. Consequently, with Geiger, who was later to collaborate with Marsden on the famous scattering experiments, Rutherford set out to find a method of recording the passage of a single alpha particle, independent of the charge it carried. The obvious method that suggested itself was the well known one of counting the scintillations produced on a zinc sulphide screen. This method was open to one serious objection — there was no way to make sure that each alpha particle that reached the screen produced a scintillation. It was possible that some of the alpha particles would impinge on the screen without causing a scintillation.

Rutherford and Geiger turned next to the ionisation chamber for a solution of their problem. Although the ionisation from a single particle could neither be measured directly nor amplified by auxiliary circuits outside the chamber, it was still possible to amplify the ionisation inside the chamber. In an ordinary ionisation chamber the voltage on the plates is just great enough to collect the ions caused by the passage of the particle. Following an observation already made for x-ray ionisation, Rutherford and Geiger decided to increase the voltage on the chamber far beyond this value, to a value so high that the plates in the chamber just did not spark over. When the voltage was applied the chamber was in a comparatively unstable condition; any small increase in voltage would cause a discharge. The electrical effect of even a single alpha particle was sufficient to set the chamber off. The number of ion pairs produced by the alpha particle in its passage through the chamber remained the same, but the ions produced, finding themselves in a strong electrical field, were immediately violently accelerated towards the electrodes. In their passage they produced more ions by collision, until the cumulative effect resulted in a charge high enough to be measurable. The chamber at such high voltage is like a loaded gun; the passage of the alpha particle merely pulls the trigger.

The ionisation chamber in which the most favorable results could be obtained differed greatly from a pair of parallel plates. A copper tube served as one electrode, and a small wire running along the diameter of the cylinder as the other. After sealing both ends of the tube the pressure of the air was reduced. The voltage required was constrained within narrow limits. Too high a voltage would cause a spark, too low a voltage would reduce the number of ions collected. Of course, it was possible to vary the voltage somewhat in the direction of reducing the ionisation; the limiting factor remained the sensitivity of the measuring instrument. The dimensions of the copper tube were also rigidly prescribed — if it was too large the random effects produced fake alpha particles; if it was too small the ionisation was not sufficient

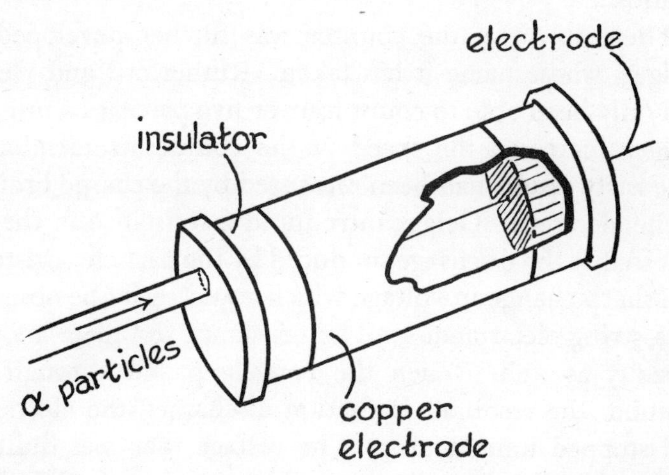

to register. But finally with the proper selection of size and voltage Rutherford and Geiger were able to count alpha particles entering the chamber as fast as three or four a minute.

The alpha particles from a small sample of radioactive material were allowed to enter the counting tube. Knowing the strength of the source and the proportion of the particles that entered the tube it was possible to count directly the amount of alpha particles given off. Rutherford found that one gram of radium produced 34,000,000,000 alpha particles every second. Subsequent measurements have raised the value to 35,000,000,000. That means that in one gram of radium 35,000,000,000 atoms disintegrate every second, providing an ample source of alpha particles for transmutation experiments.

Having devised a method which gave the number of alpha particles accurately Rutherford compared the electrical counter results with the scintillations on a zinc sulphide screen placed just where the counter had been during the experiments. Comparing the numbers from the two experiments, he showed that the screen registered every alpha particle. The absolute accuracy of the scintillation method was established.

Then, in 1913, the counter was further developed by Geiger, whose name it has taken. Rutherford and Geiger had only been able to count four or five particles a minute; Geiger increased the speed of the counter tremendously. The early results had been measured by the charge brought to the electrode. Geiger introduced a resistance in the circuit so that the discharge produced by the particle registered as a sharp change in voltage which could easily be observed on a string electrometer. The resistance served in another capacity as well. When the particle passed through the chamber the resultant ionisation discharged the electrodes and stopped immediately. The voltage then was built up only gradually through the resistance to its former high value. Had there been no resistance the voltage used by Geiger would have been enough to run a steady discharge after the first alpha particle entered. With the resistance, the counter reset itself, like an automatic rifle.

More recently the exact design of the tube has been altered, as well as the gases placed inside it. The mechanism of the discharge in a Geiger counter, like so many phenomena in gases, is not yet completely understood. As a consequence, the recipes for filling the counters with gases and treating the surfaces inside vary from one experimenter to the next. Like a good cook, each adheres to his favorite combination, swearing that no other gives such good results. Fortunately, it is the result that counts, and this soon shows whether a recipe is satisfactory.

With improvements in the tube have come improvements in the recording mechanism. After the advent of radio, the current from the Geiger tube was amplified electrically until it became strong enough to operate a mechanical recording

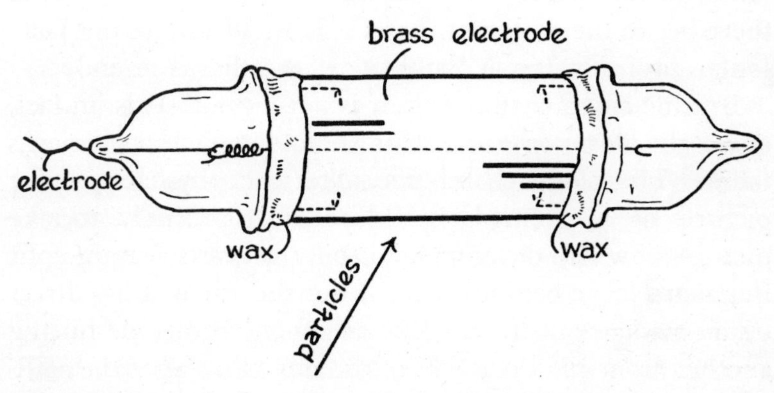

meter, an adaptation of those used by the telephone company to record the number of calls from a phone. But even these did not register quickly enough to count all the particles from an active source. At the Cavendish Laboratory radio circuits have been developed by which these meters can record particles coming as fast as 10,000 a minute – a far cry from Rutherford's first 3 or 4. Sometimes the amplified pulse operates a loud speaker in which the passage of a particle produces a sharp click. The Geiger counter has become an important and valuable instrument in nuclear research; now it is possible to hear a particle go by.

CHAPTER 12

THE CLOUD CHAMBER

THE story of the cloud chamber is the story of a Scotsman and a mist. Walking one day through a typical Scotch mist the Scotsman stopped to notice the lovely coloring of the sunlight seen through the mist. Being of an inquisitive mind, he wondered what caused the various colors. And there began the path that took C. T. R. Wilson to the Jacksonian professorship at Cambridge. All that is legend.

But the cloud chamber itself is not legend. It is, in fact, one of the most powerful tools available to nuclear physicists today. The cloud chamber enables the physicist to take pictures of the atoms he splits, or, more precisely, to take pictures of where the atom has been, the tracks that the split fragments leave behind them. Thus the scientist has direct visual evidence of the track of an atomic projectile hitting another atom and the tracks of the fragments after the collision. From these data and the fundamental laws of mechanics he is able to calculate the energy transferred in nuclear collisions.

These modern applications were far from the mind of C. T. R. Wilson as he stood that day in Scotland. For him the first step in the study of mists was their artificial formation. The method which he adopted for the formation of his clouds and the method still in use today is the sudden expansion of a gas saturated with vapor. At a given temperature air in contact with a sufficient amount of water becomes saturated with the vapor. Such a condition can be found in a half-filled water tumbler. The amount of vapor which is necessary to saturate a gas is dependent on the temperature of the system; in general, the amount in-

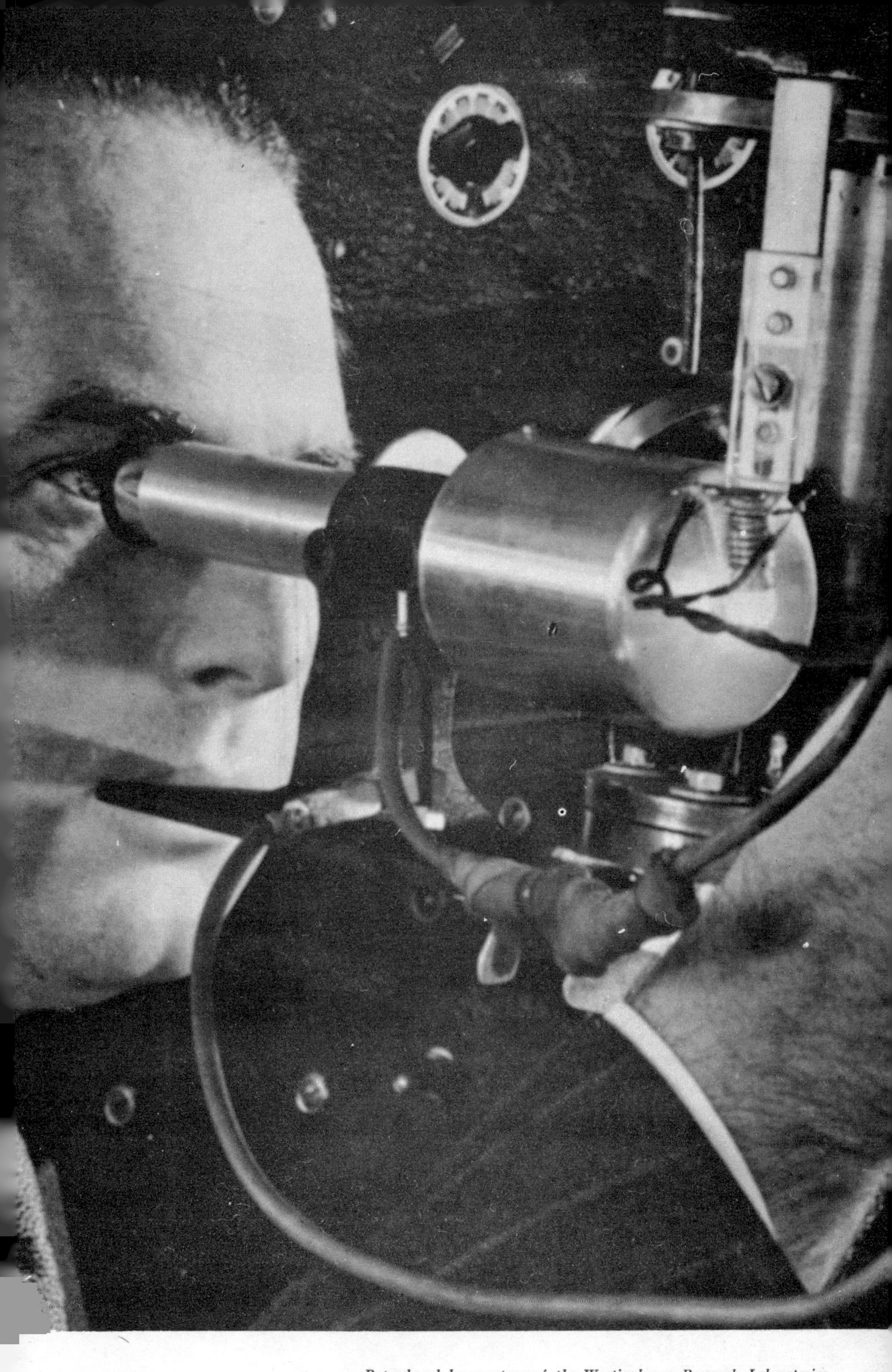

Reproduced by courtesy of the Westinghouse Research Laboratories

An electroscope in use at the target of the Westinghouse Van de Graaff generator. The movement of the metal coated fiber can be observed through the microscope eyepiece.

C. T. R. Wilson

Bunbury Smith: Reproduced by courtesy of "Discovery"

C. T. R. Wilson's 1899 model of the cloud chamber. This chamber is still used at the Cavendish for lecture demonstration.

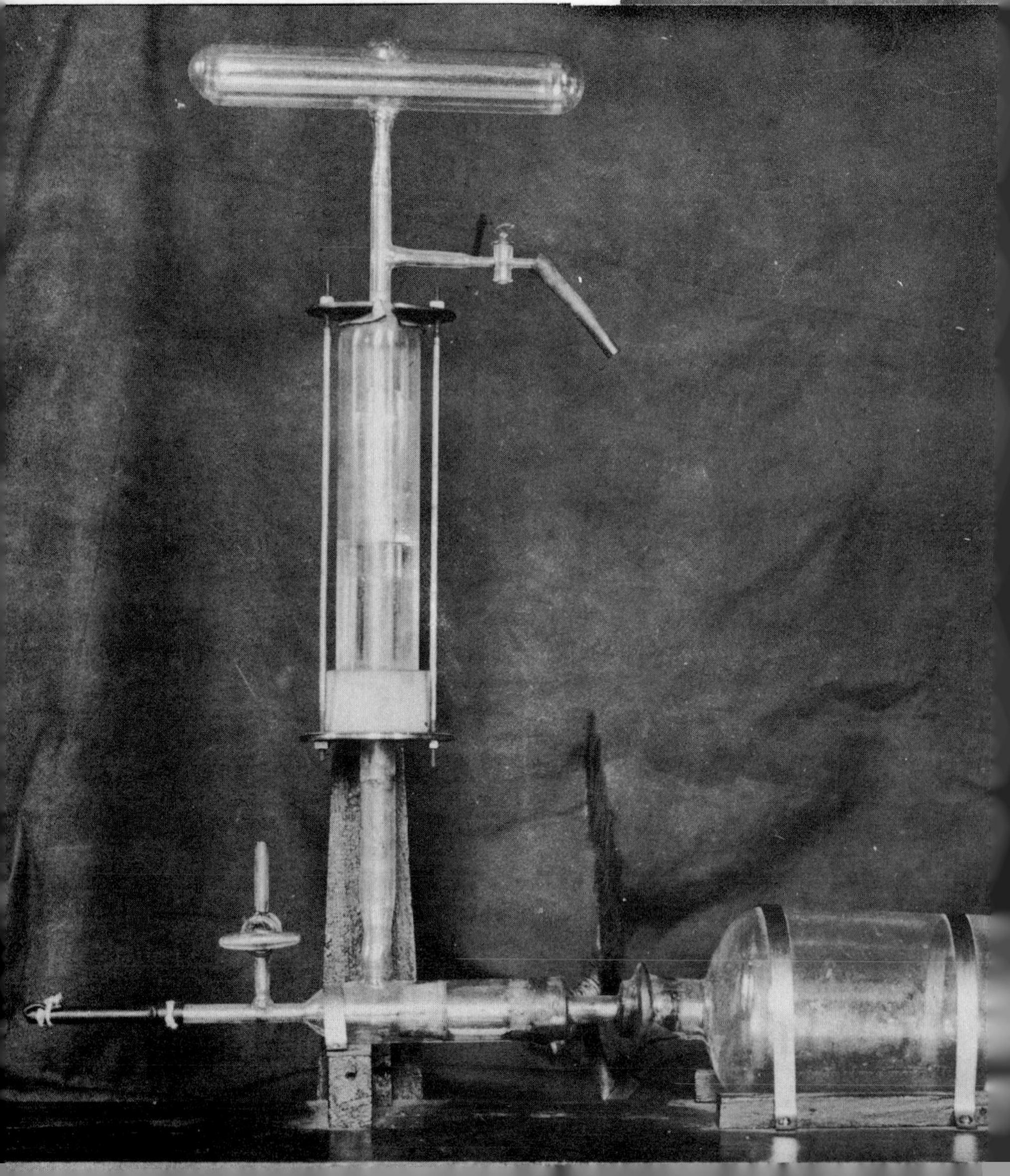

creases as the temperature becomes higher. If, in a saturated gas vapor system, the temperature is suddenly lowered, there will be an excess of vapor; and a condition called supersaturation will ensue. Depending on the degree of supersaturation the vapor will remain in the gas or else will condense in the form of raindrops or fog and remove itself from the gas.

The most important method of cooling is the expansion of gases. This, indeed, is the method used to cool all mechanical refrigerators. Consequently, it would seem best to saturate air with water vapor, cool it by sudden expansion, and so secure the necessary mist. For Wilson's experiments the easiest and neatest method of cooling was to expand the saturated vapor itself.

In his earliest work the Scotsman did indeed investigate the color of the mists. He found that under certain conditions of expansion he secured heavy mists, and he found that the colors he saw by looking at light through these mists depended on the degree of expansion, that is, on the degree of supersaturation. But far more interesting than the colors themselves was the question of the mists and the conditions of expansion under which a mist was just possible, and finally the borderline between mists and rains. There were, in fact, some expansions which would produce neither rain nor mist if the gases involved were clean.

A proper understanding of a cloud chamber requires an understanding of the term "expansion ratio." The expansion ratio is the ratio of the volume of the expanded gas to its volume just before the expansion. Thus if 10 cubic centimeters of gas are expanded to 20 cubic centimeters, the expansion ratio is 2.0; if expanded to only 12 cubic centimeters, the expansion ratio is 1.2, and so on. In his early work Wilson found that there were critical values of this expansion ratic. For expansion ratios of 1.25 or less, there was no condensation at all in clean air. With ratios slightly higher than this the condensation was in the form of a rain or droplets. But when the expansion ratio was greater than 1.38 the rain abruptly became a heavy fog. It was in these heavy fogs that the coloring was investigated.

In 1895, just two years before the publication of Wilson's first paper, Röntgen, a German scientist, had discovered the rays that bear his name, more commonly called x-rays. Wilson decided to see if the fogs were influenced by these rays. In the region of the rains, that is between the expansion ratios of 1.25 and 1.38, he found that the presence of x-rays considerably increased the number of droplets formed. In his next article in 1899 Wilson investigated the effect of the newly discovered radioactive element uranium. The rays from uranium produced the same effect as the x-rays. By this time he was convinced that the centers for the rain-like condensation were ions formed by the passage of the x-rays or the uranium rays through the air.

By 1912, Wilson had designed a new cloud chamber, the prototype of all modern cloud chambers. The diagram illustrates the mechanism. A is the cylindrical expansion chamber proper, 1 ft. in diameter, with walls and roof of glass so that the clouds may be visible. Directly below A is the piston whose abrupt descent alters the volume of gas in A and brings about the required expansion. The system of piston and cylinder is very much the same as that in an automobile engine, with the exceptions that the piston is not propelled by an explosion, and that the cylinder walls are transparent. The expansion must be rapid to provide ample cooling. After the expansion the gas in the chamber heats up at once, owing partly to conduction of heat into the gas from the walls of the cloud chamber. If the expansion is slow, the gas will have begun to heat up during the expansion. Wilson secured his sudden expansion by the instantaneous removal of all the air below the piston. With no air to support it the piston drops like a shot bird, pushed faster by the pressure

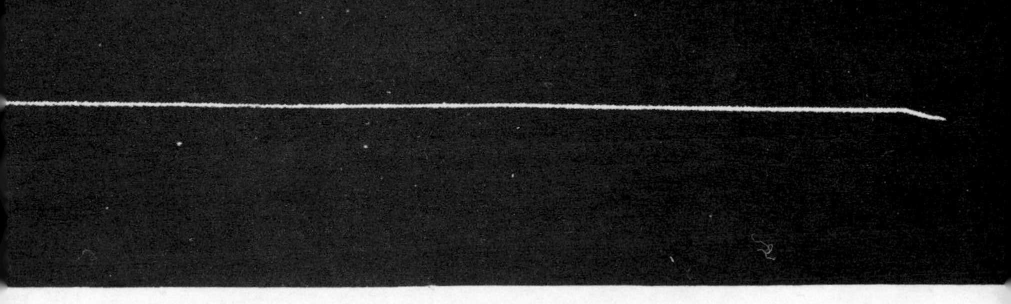

Reproduced by permission from "Radiations from Radioactive Substances," by Rutherford, Chadwick, and Ellis: Cambridge University Press; The Macmillan Company

Track of an alpha particle. The change in direction is due to elastic collision with another nucleus in the cloud chamber.

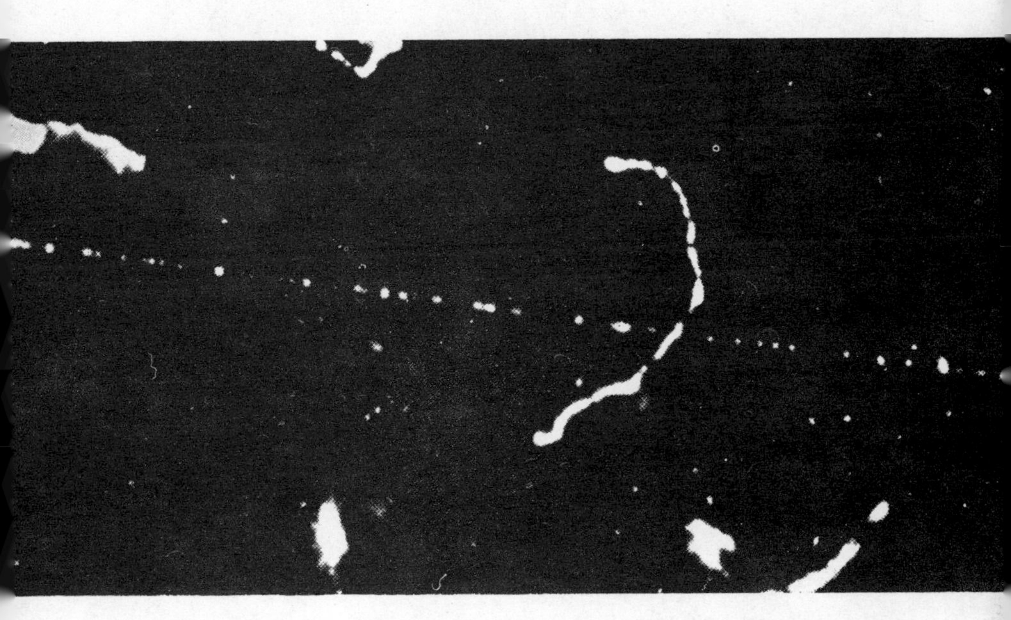

Reproduced by permission from "Discovery"

ast beta particle track shooting across chamber with far less ionisation than alpha particle track.

lpha particles emitted from actinium emanation and actinium A. The two parallel tracks are ie positive and negative ions formed by the alpha particle from actinium emanation, already parated. The sharp track shooting diagonally across is an alpha particle given off by actinium A, about 1/500th of a second later.

Reproduced by permission from "Discovery"

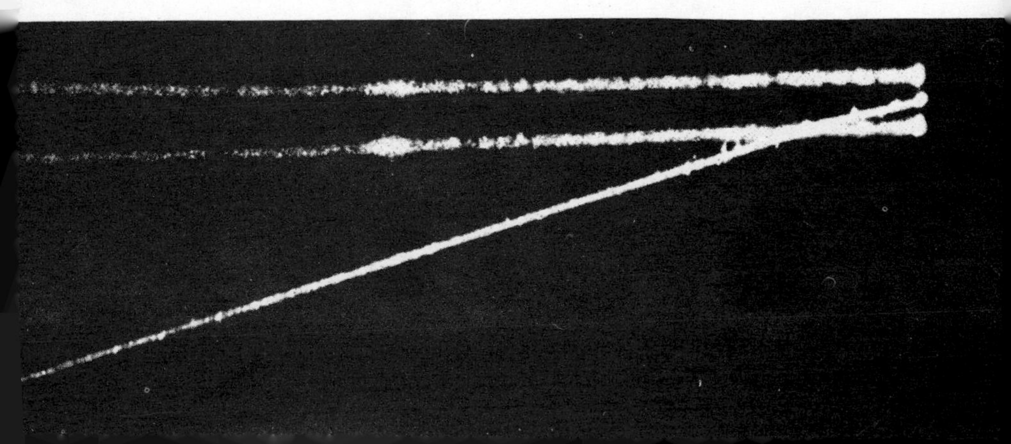

Reproduced by courtesy of "Discovery"

1912 model cloud chamber.

A modern cloud chamber.

Reprinted by courtesy of "Discovery"

of air in the chamber A above it. So that the air may be removed suddenly, the space below the piston is connected by wide tubing to the flask C. The entrance to the flask is closed by a rubber stopper B, which can be opened by a sharp pull on a rod connected to B from the outside. In operating the chamber, all the air is pumped out of C, and the valve B opened to its full extent. The air then rushes

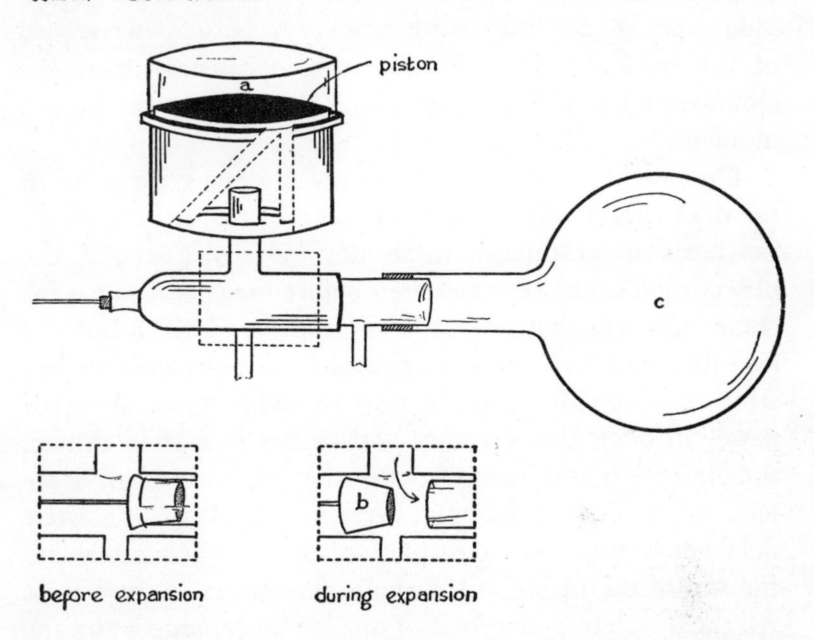

out of the space below the piston into the empty flask and the piston descends rapidly.

Wilson found that the drops in the rain-like expansion form on ions. Dust particles also cause the formation of droplets – this is largely what happens in an ordinary rain storm – but once the chamber has been cleaned of dust, the centers that remain for the formation of droplets are ions. It is this feature which makes the chamber so important in nuclear physics. Each ion serves for the formation of one droplet. Counting the number of droplets gives the number of ions.

An alpha particle fired into a cloud chamber immediately after the expansion would cause condensation of droplets on all the ions left in its wake, leaving as mark of its passage a narrow trail of closely clustered droplets. To make the droplets visible, or the track of the alpha particle visible, light from a strong mercury arc lamp is sent through the chamber, and the bottom of the chamber is painted black to provide contrast for the white track. A permanent record of the track is provided by setting a camera above the cloud chamber and photographing the track at the proper moment.

The phrase, "the proper moment," hides a great many of the difficulties of cloud chamber technique. Since the chamber heats up so quickly, in about 1/50th of a second, the observations must be completed before the chamber has become so warm that the drops disappear. This is but the first difficulty. The next is caused by the presence of any stray radiation that may be near by. Any radiation which passes through the chamber and causes ionisation during the expansion will leave tracks made up of very small droplets. Such stray tracks must be removed. A weak electric field between the top glass plate of the cloud chamber and the top of the piston will remove the effects of these rays. All the droplets, being formed on ions, are charged, and the electric field attracts these charged droplets. Consequently some, say the negatively charged ions, will rise to the top of the chamber, and the others, the positively charged ones, will sink to the bottom. Here they condense on the walls and no longer interfere with other tracks. Since the tracks are formed equally of positively and negatively charged particles, the effect of the electric field is first a broadening of the track, and then finally a separation of the ions into two groups, one negative, rising towards the top of the chamber, the other, positive, sinking towards the bottom of the chamber.

Once the expansion is complete, the drops form very quickly on the ions. These large drops are so heavy that they move very slowly in the electric field, so slowly that they appear still. This places another limitation on "the proper moment," for the alpha ray must be shot into the chamber immediately after the expansion so that the track has no chance to disperse. If it is shot in before the expansion is complete, the ions will begin to separate before they are immobilized by the drops. If it waits too long after the expansion, the chamber will be too hot to form any droplets.

To perform all the operations in the proper sequence a delicate timing mechanism is necessary. Wilson used an ingenious arrangement with a falling weight which first pulled out the plug B and allowed the expansion to take place, then let the particles into the chamber, and finally made a contact which flashed on the arc light at the proper moment for taking the picture. The photograph reproduced illustrates "the proper moment" by showing one perfectly defined track and one partially dispersed. The radioactive element, actinium emanation, disintegrates into actinium A and an alpha particle. Within a time interval of the order of 1/500th of a second, actinium A again disintegrates, giving off another alpha particle. When the expansion was made the actinium emanation atom had already disintegrated and shot off an alpha particle whose track can be seen already dispersed as the two parallel heavy tracks towards the top of the photograph. The remaining atom, actinium A, recoiled a small distance, which accounts for its not being exactly in the center of the dispersed alpha tracks. Then it immediately ejected another alpha particle whose track, sharply defined, shoots across the picture diagonally.

The modern modifications of the cloud chamber are few.

Wilson himself is responsible for the insertion of a rubber diaphragm instead of a piston. When the air below the diaphragm is exhausted, the rubber diaphragm is sucked down and this provides the necessary expansion in the chamber above. The operation of the mechanism has changed considerably, and Wilson's falling weight has been replaced by an electrical timing system. After expansion these systems reset the cloud chamber so that it is immediately ready for another operation. True determination of the paths of the particles is possible only if they can be located accurately in space inside the chamber. Wilson had already used two cameras set at an angle in order to obtain a stereoscope view of the chamber. Reprojection of the stereoscopic pictures shows the paths in space of the particles participating in nuclear reactions.

With the Geiger counter the scientist can hear the particles as they pass; with the cloud chamber he can see them. No matter how great the arguments that can be deduced from figures and calculations, the scientist, like the man in the street, is most easily convinced by what he sees. Possibly for this reason the cloud chamber has proved its importance as an instrument in recent nuclear discoveries. Each of the other apparatus which can be used to identify and measure particle paths usually gives only a single piece of information at one time, the range or the size of a particle, or the direction of its track. But the cloud chamber provides all these, and more, at once; and furthermore, the cloud chamber provides them visually. The dramatic immediacy of the cloud chamber photograph sets it off as compelling and incontrovertible evidence.

Smashing the atom would have been of little value if its results could not have been interpreted. That this interpretation should result from the experiments of one Scotsman in a mist shows how unpredictable scientific application may be. The cloud chamber, the most powerful instrument

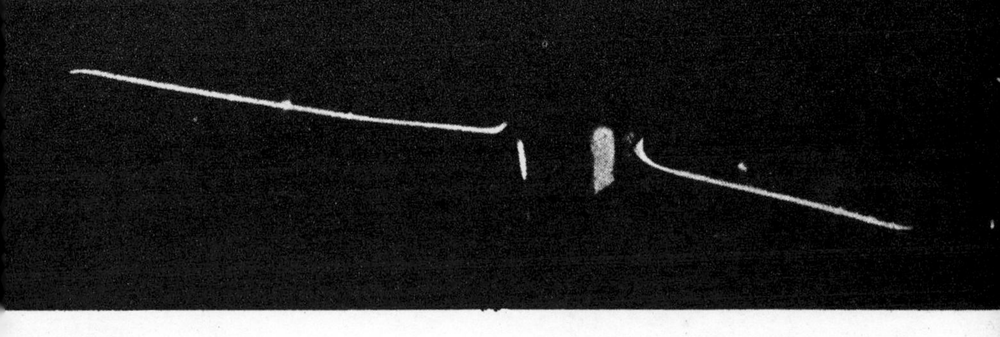

Reproduced by permission from "Discovery"

Tracks of two alpha particles emitted in the disintegration of lithium by protons. The apparently formless mass in the center of the picture is the lithium target let down in a recess in the top of the chamber. The alpha particles are emitted in opposite directions, and the curve at their origin is due to turbulence in the gas during the expansion.

Disintegration of nitrogen by alpha particles. A single alpha particle among the forest of trails meets a nitrogen nucleus. The forked track shows the results, with the newly formed oxygen going off in one direction — as shown by the heavy track — and the ejected proton going off in another direction along the lighter track.

Reproduced by permission from "Radiations from Radioactive Substances": by Rutherford, Chadwick, and Ellis, Cambridge University Press, The Macmillan Company

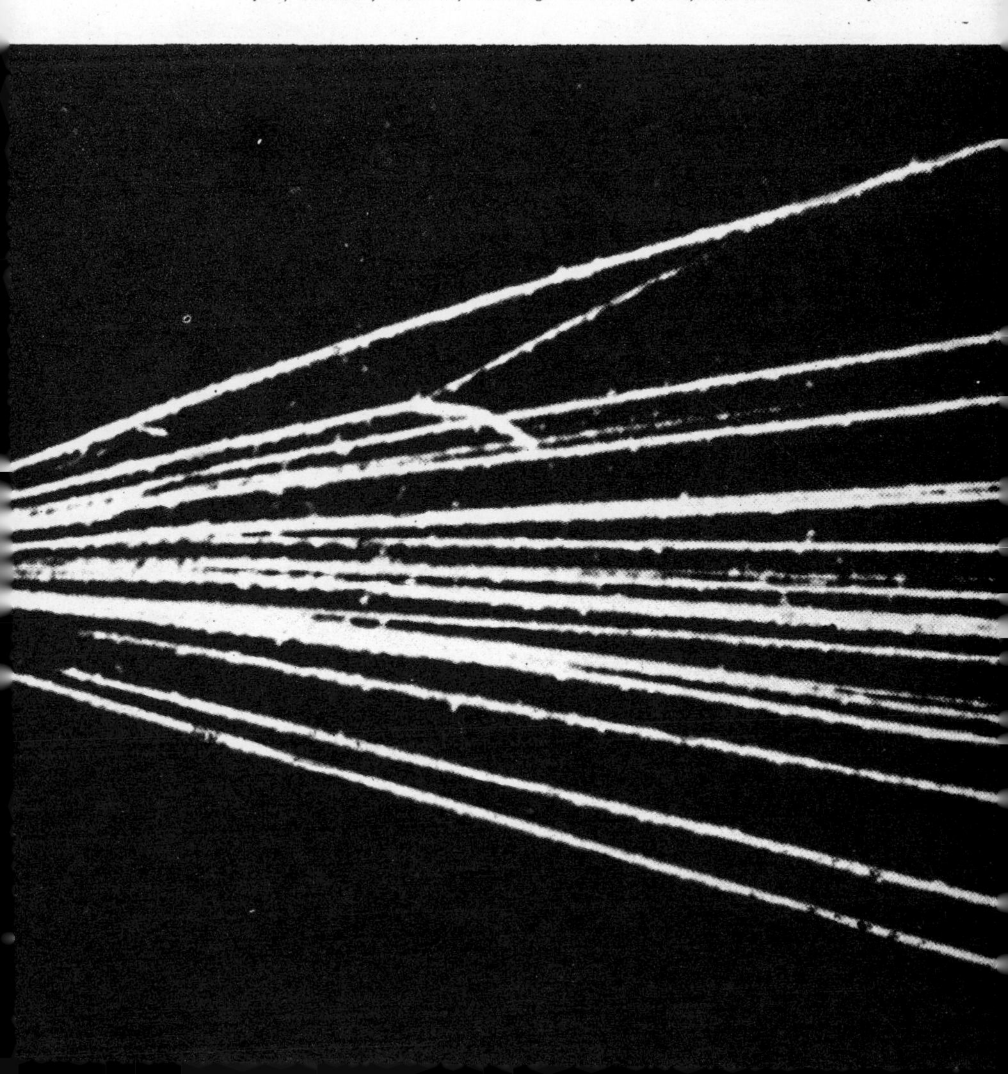

H. R. Crane: Reproduced by courtesy of the "Journal of Applied Physic

Tracks of electrons in a cloud chamber in a magnetic field.

Tracks of positrons in a cloud chamber in a magnetic field. The tracks going in the wro direction are electrons that have strayed into the picture.

H. R. Crane: Reproduced by courtesy of the "Journal of Applied Physic

in understanding nuclear reactions, has developed from a field investigated long before the nucleus was conceived. Here, as so often in science, researches begun with divergent purposes have yielded results which converge on the solution of a problem outstanding in importance.

PART III
WHY SMASH THE ATOM?

F. W. Goro for Life Magazine

Enrico Fermi in 1939.

Dever from Black Star

Otto Hahn.

CHAPTER 13

URANIUM FISSION

EARLY in 1939 the scientific world was shocked by a new discovery. The new discovery – an unprecedented atomic explosion in the uranium atom called fission – was shocking because it offered a completely new interpretation of a process that most physicists thought was already explained in simpler terms. The artificial disintegration of uranium, an element which is also naturally radioactive, had been investigated in some detail and it seemed that a complete understanding of the process required only the explanation of a few small discrepancies. A few scientists in Germany and France continued research on the uranium problem, but in the main, scientific attention was directed towards other apparently more interesting fields. Then when finally these few scientists announced the discovery of the fission of uranium, a hitherto unheard of breakup of the uranium atom that liberated tremendous energy, the announcement fell on scientific ears like a bombshell. The confusion in the uranium atom when it broke up so spectacularly was no greater than that in the scientific world when the announcement was made.

Uranium fission would not have been discovered had it not been for the great advance in nuclear knowledge between 1932 and 1939. Contribution to this knowledge has not resulted from disintegration experiments alone. In fact, the discovery of one fundamental particle came about from the investigation of cosmic radiation — a field only distantly related to atom smashing. Cosmic radiation is itself a complex and interesting subject, and the cosmic ray is probably the most energetic radiation known to man. These rays originate in space, away from the earth; both their great intensity and the riddle of their formation have excited considerable research. One very important result of this research was the discovery in 1932 of the positron — a positive electron. The positron was a very welcome find, for not only had theory predicted its existence, but also the positron gave a little more symmetry to the particles already known. Scientists had always objected vaguely to the analogy between proton and electron, for it seemed strange that equivalent charges opposite in sign should find themselves associated with masses so disparate. The positive electron did away with this objection. It was truly the positive analogue of the electron, having identical mass and identical charge, differing only in the sign of its charge.

For perfect symmetry one would demand the discovery of a negative proton following upon that of a positive electron. But such a particle has not yet been found on earth; it hardly remains to be discovered, for with a large mass and a negative charge it should be easily observable. There is good evidence for the existence of a heavy negative particle intermediate in mass between the electron and the proton in cosmic ray research, but such a particle has never yet been observed as a participant in any nuclear reactions.

The positron, however, does occur in nuclear reactions; its discovery in these reactions is closely associated with another important discovery. Curie and Joliot had found that aluminum emitted positrons when it was bombarded with alpha particles from polonium — the same alpha particles they had used in investigating the neutron. Once the positron had been discovered it was easily distinguishable from the electron. In a magnetic field the curvature of the path of the particles even with identical energy differs radically, for positrons are curved in one direction and electrons in another. The amount of the curvature is the same; only the direction differs. The difference is clearly demonstrable in a cloud chamber. When the chamber is placed in a magnetic field, the ion trails indicate at a glance the sign of the particles.

Curie and Joliot soon noticed one striking fact: the positrons were still given off even after the alpha particle source had been removed. The positron emission behaved like the

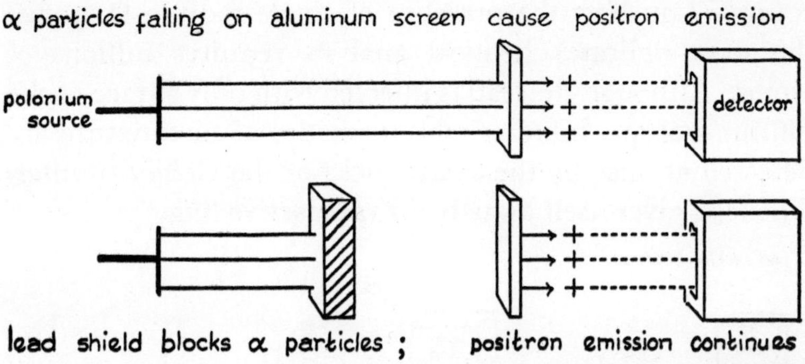

α particles falling on aluminum screen cause positron emission

polonium source

detector

lead shield blocks α particles ; positron emission continues

negative electron radiation given off by natural radioactive substances; it decayed with a characteristic half-life. Concluding that the alpha particles had induced artificial radioactivity in the aluminum, Curie and Joliot reported to the French Academy on January 15, 1934, that, "for the first time it has been possible with the aid of an exterior cause to create radioactivity in atomic nuclei. . . ."

This was a great discovery. Although physicists were still unable to alter the rate of radioactive decay they had learned how to make stable elements radioactive. Radioactivity had already provided the instrument with which the nature of the nucleus was first investigated. Now a new artificial radioactivity had been provided with which far more knowledge about the nucleus could be gained.

Previous work on natural radioactivity had shown that it was impossible to separate a radioactive isotope from an inactive isotope by chemical means. Radium D, which is radioactive, and lead, which is not, are isotopes; once a small amount of radium D is added to the lead the pair are inseparable. Isotopic only with lead, radium D is readily separable from all the other elements. Their union is of great value in tracing small quantities of lead infected with radium D. Though the amounts of lead are so small as to defy chemical analysis, the companion radium D by its radioactivity immediately reveals the presence of the lead. The Geiger counter can show the presence of single radium D atoms; the most delicate chemical analysis requires billions of atoms. Although the lead is infected with only a trace of the radium isotope, infinitesimal quantities of the mixture are detected at once by the sharp clicks of the Geiger counter. The lead gives itself away by its radioactive fingerprints.

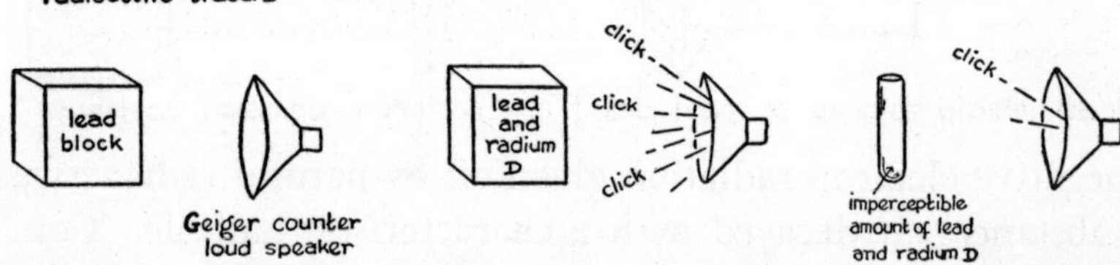

Before Curie and Joliot's discovery it had only been possible to identify the product of a transmutation by physical means. To find the mass of the resultant nucleus required an accurate knowledge of the mass and energy of the invading particle, the struck nucleus, and the expelled particle. Such knowledge could be obtained from pictures taken in the cloud chamber, where the range, and hence the energy, of the expelled particle could be determined. Now with the discovery of artificial radioactivity the product nuclei could be identified chemically: this Curie and Joliot did and reported in their next paper. After a chemical precipitation it was easy to tell whether the radioactive element was in the precipitate or remained in the solution. After separating them, each was brought to the counter. If the activity was only in the precipitate, the counter would remain mute when the solution was set before it, but would begin to count as soon as the precipitate came near. Analyses that had never before been possible could now be made for traces of elements if they could be fingerprinted by radioactivity. It was usually necessary to add a certain amount of the element which was suspected to be an isotope as a carrier, otherwise the radioactivity might get lost by absorption on walls of vessels or other mechanical loss during the operations. If after a series of stringent chemical separations the radioactivity was inseparable from the carrier there could be no doubt that the fugitive was isotopic with it.

Three months later confirmation of artificial radioactivity came from a different quarter. In a letter to *Nature* dated April 10, Enrico Fermi of the University of Rome, a brilliant theoretician as well as experimentalist, announced that he had produced artificial radioactivity in a long series of elements which he irradiated with neutrons. An intimate mixture of radon gas, a source of alpha particles, and beryllium powder provided the neutrons, which in turn fell on targets of the element to be investigated. After the neutron source had been removed, radiation from the target decayed as expected, with a normal half-life. Experiments had already been carried out by others on the production of artificial radioactivity by proton and deuteron bombardment, but only a limited number of elements with low atomic number exhibited the desired activity. With neutrons, though, almost every element could be made radioactive, irrespective of its place in the atomic number system. Fermi surmised correctly that the neutron was so effective because its lack of charge permitted easy penetration of the nucleus.

Further examination of the properties of neutron activation led to still another startling result. When the speed of the neutron was reduced by passage through matter, more especially hydrogenous matter like water and paraffin, the efficiency of the neutrons in producing activation was usually increased by a large factor. Immersion of the neutron source in a large beaker of water often enhanced the radioactivity produced. The effect may be explained on the assumption that the nucleus has a particular affinity for neutrons of low energy. The experiment of Professor Bohr in which marbles finally come to rest in a saucer was devised to demonstrate slow neutron penetration rather than that of fast neutrons. When a slow neutron is captured by the nucleus, there usually is not enough excess energy to throw off another particle at once; instead the excess is radiated as gamma rays. Capture of the neutron results in formation of an isotope of the element heavier by one unit than the stable one. Extra weight introduced into the nucleus may make the new atom somewhat unstable. Artificial radioactivity is an instability intermediate between immediate disintegration and complete stability; in fact, the captured neutron often contributes just enough additional energy to cause radioactivity. The new element may return to normal only after emitting an electron whose loss means an increase of one in positive nuclear charge. The charge of this new element, the one next higher on the atomic number scale, is more compatible with the additional weight of the added neutron.

The number of electrons emitted from the newly formed radioactive element decays at a definite rate. Like natural radioactive elements, the new ones have distinctive half-lives with values given by the time required for the rate of emission of electrons to diminish by half. Although more than three hundred new radioactive isotopes can be made artificially, the half-lives of these isotopes can not be predicted in advance. The time required for the artificial radioactivity to die away varies according to some as yet unknown arrangement of elementary particles inside the nucleus.

Fermi found that the neutron could penetrate even the uranium nucleus, the heaviest of all known elements with an atomic number of 92. Uranium, normally radioactive, disintegrates with the emission of an alpha particle; after the capture of a neutron it gives off an electron instead. Emission of an electron increases the atomic number by one to form an unknown element of number 93. This seemed truly a new element, for no element of number greater than 92 had ever been found before on earth. Such new artificial elements, higher on the scale than uranium, are called trans-uranic elements. Production of new elements did not cease with element 93. It also disintegrated in turn and gave birth to a series of radioactivities which included elements 94, 95, and 96. These elements were identified as trans-uranic because they did not possess the chemical properties of any of the elements with numbers from 86 to 92. It was to be expected that neutron capture by uranium would produce a neighboring element since this had always been the case with other elements: any other conclusion was unthinkable. Furthermore there was some evidence that the new elements behaved chemically as might be predicted for trans-uranic elements. Absolute identification of a radioactive element is usually co-precipitation with a known isotope of that element. Thus radium D is absolutely identified as an isotope of lead, because, once mixed, it is always precipitated with, and inseparable from, lead; and it can be separated from all other elements with comparative ease. With the new elements it was impossible to carry out so stringent a test, since they were elements never before known, and could not be tested by co-precipitation with any existent element. On the basis of this reasoning it was generally conceded that the elements that Fermi had discovered were indeed trans-uranic, new elements, hitherto unknown.

There were as many as ten radioactive periods associated with these new elements, and for some time chemical research was carried on in order to pin down the activities and to find the radioactive family, exactly as had been done in the natural radioactive series. The work was exacting and difficult, since new methods had to be devised for new elements. In 1937, Otto Hahn, head of the Kaiser Wilhelm Institute for Chemistry in Berlin, with his co-workers, Miss Meitner and Strassmann, had found some order among the elements and arranged them in three series. Shortly thereafter, Madame Curie-Joliot in Paris and a collaborator discovered a new trans-uranic element resulting from the bombardment of uranium with neutrons. This new element refused to fit in the series already worked out by Hahn, and several alternatives to the Hahn scheme were proposed, none very satisfactory. Then early in November, 1938, Hahn repeated the Curie experiment and found not only the element with the three and a half hour period which had been observed in Paris, but also a new activity. Hahn's new element emitted heavy alpha particles, in striking contrast to the light positrons and electrons that had previously been known in induced radioactivity. Another startling feature in Hahn's discovery was that his new element appeared to be a radium isotope: radium can only be formed from uranium by the emission of two alpha particles, and such a process had never been known to follow neutron capture. A better explanation was required, and more research was necessary.

Consequently Hahn went to work to investigate the properties of the new activity. The standard procedure for tracing small amounts of radium chemically is to add barium, which is very similar to radium, and carry out all the separations of barium with the accompanying radium from the nearby elements. When this separation is finished the radium itself is removed from the barium. The new radioactivity behaved as expected, and separated cleanly from all the other possible elements. But when the time came to separate the activity from the barium, it couldn't be done. Radium could be separated, but the new radioactivity stuck to the barium even more tightly than radium. On physical grounds it seemed unthinkable that the new radioactivity could belong to an element so light as barium. It would mean that instead of merely giving off an alpha particle, the irradiated uranium had divided itself into two almost equal parts, a veritable atomic rupture. Yet on chemical grounds it seemed certain that the radioactivity belonged to barium. In a paper published the 6th of January, 1939, Hahn and Strassmann wrote, "As chemists we must really say that the new bodies do not behave like radium, rather like barium. . . . As nuclear chemists we can not bring ourselves to take this step so contradictory to all the experience of nuclear physics."

Then ten days later there came a letter to *Nature* signed by Miss Meitner, now exiled from Germany, and Frisch of the Institute of Theoretical Physics which Professor Bohr heads in Copenhagen. Even after Miss Meitner had left Germany, Hahn and Strassmann were careful to mention in their publication that much of the work they did was expedited by the methods she had developed. In Copenhagen, Miss Meitner and Frisch had taken the step and suggested that the uranium nucleus did break up into two halves. This nucleus, so heavy already, did not have much stability of form. The addition of just one more neutron, like the proverbial straw, was enough to break the

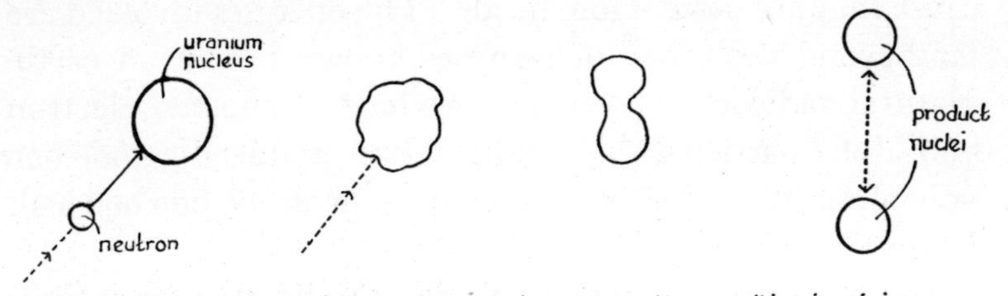

neutron penetrates uranium nucleus causing deformation resulting in fission

uranium. To explain the fission, Meitner and Frisch suggested that the nucleus behaved like a water drop which, when it gets too large, breaks up into drops each almost equal in size. At the same time Frisch wrote another letter giving experimental confirmation of the occurrence of the process. When the uranium nucleus breaks up tremendous amounts of energy are liberated, so great is the excess in mass of the uranium over that of the two resultant particles. If fission occurs, the presence of uranium in an ionisation chamber should give rise to peaks in the recording instrument much higher than those observed from the passage of ordinary alpha particles, since the new particles, far heavier than alpha particles, have energies of the order of 100,000,000 electron volts. As he had expected, Frisch found pulses on his recording oscilloscope so large that they could only be produced by the fission of the uranium nucleus.

The energy release which accompanies uranium fission is far greater than ever has been known before. An energy of 100,000,000 volts produced artificially on earth by the capture of a neutron is a figure just as startling to physicists as to laymen. No comparable process is known; no particles of such great mass have ever been liberated before. Fission occurs with thorium as well as uranium, and occurs on the capture of other particles besides neutrons. But elements lower in atomic number than thorium have not yet been found to break up in this astounding fashion, probably because they are more stable inside. The energies involved are far beyond the range of energies known before on earth. Natural radioactive elements produce 14,000,000 electron volt alpha particles, the cyclotron has produced 32,000,000 volt alpha particles, but fission produces 100,000,000 volt barium particles.

But the story did not end there. Publication takes time, and Meitner and Frisch's letter did not appear until the 11th of February. Meanwhile Frisch had communicated some preliminary results to Professor Bohr, who had come to America. Professor Fermi was already in New York, and after discussion between Bohr and Fermi the experiment

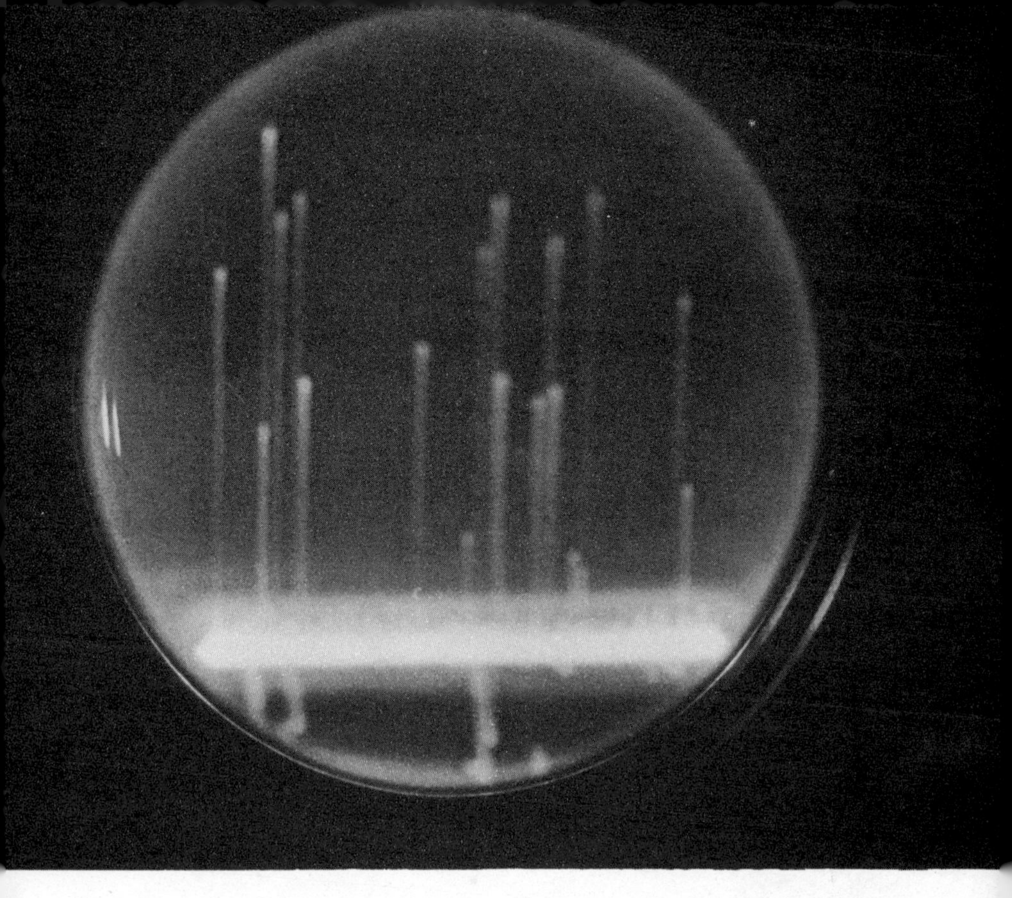

F. W. Goro for Life Magazine

aks from the fission of uranium. The black halation at the bottom of the picture conceals
: alpha particle peaks. The varying heights of the peaks due to fission show the range of
energies with which the particles are given off.

J. R. Dunning: Reproduced by courtesy of the "Journal of Applied Physics"

Associated Press

Niels Bohr in 1937.

made independently by Frisch was undertaken at Columbia on the 25th of January. At that time there was a scientific meeting in Washington and Professors Bohr and Fermi discussed the recent work of Hahn and Strassmann. Immediate confirmation of uranium fission was obtained at the Department of Terrestrial Magnetism in Washington and the whole startling story appeared in the newspapers. At once further confirmation came from other laboratories scattered from Baltimore to California.

On the first of February, *Le Temps,* in Paris, carried in its routine notice of the weekly meeting of the French Academy of Sciences a dry report that Mme. Curie-Joliot and M. Joliot had independently by parallel and different means obtained the phenomenon of uranium fission. Joliot's paper had been completed in time for presentation to the meeting on the 30th of January, which meant that his independent research had been carried out almost at the same time that Frisch was completing work in Copenhagen. In England the first news came in an article in the London *Times* on February first which carried an account of the American experiments; and the same day a copy of Joliot's paper arrived at the Cavendish. The phenomenon of fission was so striking that it was easy to repeat the experiment and see it for ourselves. A small quantity of uranium was put in an ionisation chamber and the recording oscilloscope showed the normal small peaks due to the natural alpha particles given off by the uranium. As soon as a neutron beam fell on the uranium, a number of tall peaks appeared. We had watched uranium fission.

CHAPTER 14

ATOM SMASHING

THE operation of a cyclotron is a complex and varied experience. The vagaries of so complex a machine are unpredictable. But the daily operation of the cyclotron and similar atom smashing machines is a necessity for nuclear physics. Without them it is impossible to provide the long groundwork of experiment that is required before new discoveries are possible. If the cyclotron is in good working order, running it for a day may be pure routine. But when trouble does develop, a day at the cyclotron may become a long series of unhappy disasters. When the scientist comes to work in the morning he can't tell how he will feel when he goes home.

Before work is begun, the vacuum must be good enough for the bombarding deuterons to circulate without bumping into too many other particles. If there is a leak in the tank and the gauges indicate that the pressure is too high the leak must be found and sealed before the cyclotron can be turned on. Sometimes experience will indicate where the leak is, but far more often finding it is a tedious, nerve-racking job. Leaks are far too small to be seen or heard, they must be found blindly, by relying on the sensitive vacuum gauges to show when anything done to the tank affects the pressure. The scientist looking for a leak is like a blind man hunting for a black hat in the dark.

If there are no leaks, or after the leaks have been sealed, the water valve is opened. As the water flows through the system, dividing among the many cooling circuits, all the electrical relays that indicate satisfactory water flow come into action. The sound of clicking relays is clearly audible

P. Donaldson

The Harvard cyclotron with a beam of deuterons emerging into the air. On the right can be seen some of the valves for adjusting the water flow in the cooling system. On the left can be seen the system for controlling the gas flow into the cyclotron. This was operated remotely from the control room. The microphone was connected into the control room. The grill behind it is a safety device to keep one from accidental contact with the deflector (voltage about 100,000).

Close-up showing the beam as it emerges into the air. The meter stick was a common device for measuring the voltage of the beam. Penetration of a deuteron beam 63 centimeters into the air indicates about 9,600,000 electron volt particles. To this must be added a small amount for the loss in penetrating the thin aluminum foil that seals the window.

P. Donaldson

P. Donaldson

Operating a gate in the Harvard cyclotron target chamber. This gate is a vacuum tight joint which can be used to shut the target chamber off from the rest of the cyclotron. Thus a target can be changed without loss of the main vacuum. The two glass windows are for inspection.

Putting a target on the cyclotron. At the back of the target chamber the aluminum window (a little wrinkled) may be seen. The operator is holding the target plate by its water cooling tubes.

P. Donaldson

above the hiss of the water. The power used by a cyclotron is so great that most of its parts must be properly cooled; the relays register any failure in the water supply and immediately turn the cyclotron off before it can get too hot. Until all the relays are closed the cyclotron can not be turned on: as long as they remain closed, the water system needs no further attention.

The cyclotron is powered by three huge generators. As they are turned on their whine adds another note to the increasing din. The magnet, however, and its attendant generator can not be turned on until a careful check has been made for any stray pieces of iron around the magnet. There are several glass windows let into the cyclotron tank so that the position of the dees can be observed from outside. Stray iron left around a cyclotron, attracted inexorably by the powerful magnet, has been known to be snatched through one of these windows. Not only does a shattered window mean a loss of the precious vacuum, but, what is more important, it means that the inside of the tank will be littered with glass fragments. Cleaning a cyclotron is neither an easy nor a pleasant job.

When the filaments in the various radio tubes have been lighted, the cyclotron is ready for operation. Rather, it is ready for a preliminary operation, for it is first necessary to de-gas. Although it has stood idle only overnight, with high speed vacuum pumps constantly in operation, the metal surfaces in the radio tubes and the cyclotron have picked up gas. As the power is turned on, the surfaces heat up and give off once again the gas they have absorbed in the night. A burst of gas may cause the vacuum relay to release, which turns off the power. After the gas has been pumped away the power is turned on again and more gas driven off, until finally all of it has been driven out of the metal surfaces.

Only when all the gas that isn't wanted has been eliminated can the gas that is wanted, the heavy hydrogen from which deuterons are made, be let into the cyclotron. The gas valve is opened electrically and the pressure adjusted to its usual value. When the cyclotron filament and its accessory voltage have been turned on, the deuterons are formed in the center of the tank, waiting their long spiral journey inside the dees. Then the main power is switched on and the deuterons begin their travel as the voltage alternates from dee to dee. But the particles can't get out until the deflector voltage is applied. Then, if the current through the magnet is adjusted to the critical value, a beam may appear. When finally, the needle begins to move along the face of the beam meter, it is a very welcome sight. As the beam is increased to a maximum by further adjustment, the note of the generator changes its pitch, with the additional load required to spin the particles around.

Even when the beam is at a maximum, the cyclotroneer's task is not complete. The adjustments are critical and the cyclotron after a period of rest is always unsteady. The sparks that often occur inside set off bursts of gas which switch off the high voltage supply through the vacuum relay. The many metal parts heat up, and as they heat, warp. Then the tuning must be adjusted to compensate for the change. All the noises that accompany a cyclotron's operation may be heard through the loud-speaker system that connects it to the distant control desk – any slight change in sound may demand immediate attention. Sometimes even the array of meters on the control desk is not sufficient. When the cyclotron is finally functioning properly the operator can relax his vigilance and run the machine with occasional adjustments in the critical tuning.

Production of a radioactive isotope, like radioactive sodium with its characteristic 14.8 hour half-life, requires preparation of a target suitable for mounting in the cyclotron. The sodium must be held tightly and cooled adequately in vertical position directly in front of the cyclotron beam. If sodium metal is used, great care must be taken, since sodium melts easily, and the beam is strong enough to melt holes even in copper foil. Usually targets made of low melting materials are kept in an extra target chamber, separated from the cyclotron proper by a thin aluminum window transparent to the beam of deuterons. If there is an accident to the target, or if particles of sodium are sprayed off owing to the impact of the swift deuterons, it is only necessary to clean the subsidiary target chamber. Should the contamination enter the cyclotron chamber proper, its removal would be a difficult and delicate job.

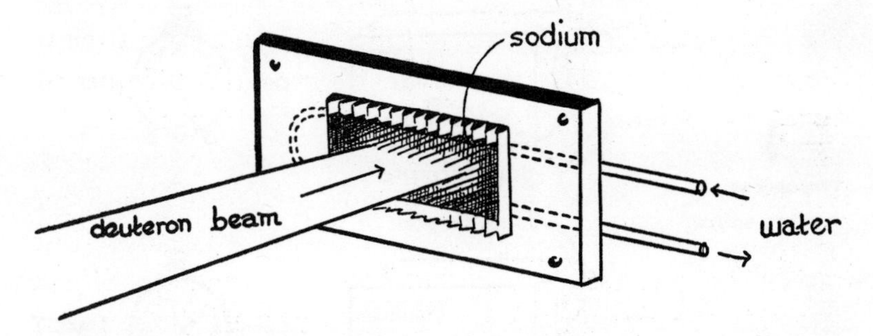

The target may consist of a water cooled plate with several deep grooves in the middle so that the sodium, pressed tightly against the grooves, will adhere to them for support and better cooling. This plate is screwed onto the end of the target chamber with the sodium directly exposed to the deuteron beam and the bombardment is begun.

The total exposure to the deuteron beam is measured by a beam integrator, an electrical device that punctuates the waiting time by repeated clicks, each click signifying a given amount of bombardment as registered on an appropriate meter. The clicks, coming rapidly one after the other, provide merry music, usually indicating that all is well. After the target has had the necessary exposure it is removed and the intensity of radiation measured as soon as possible. The sodium is taken from the water cooled target plate and run through a series of chemical separations to free it from impurities, especially other radioactivities it may have acquired during bombardment. The chemical separations must be rapid, lest the radioactivity decay too greatly during the chemistry.

The purified sample is then brought up to a Geiger counter for determination of its half-life. The counter can not be kept close to the cyclotron, for the stray radiation from a cyclotron is so intense that it would make a Geiger

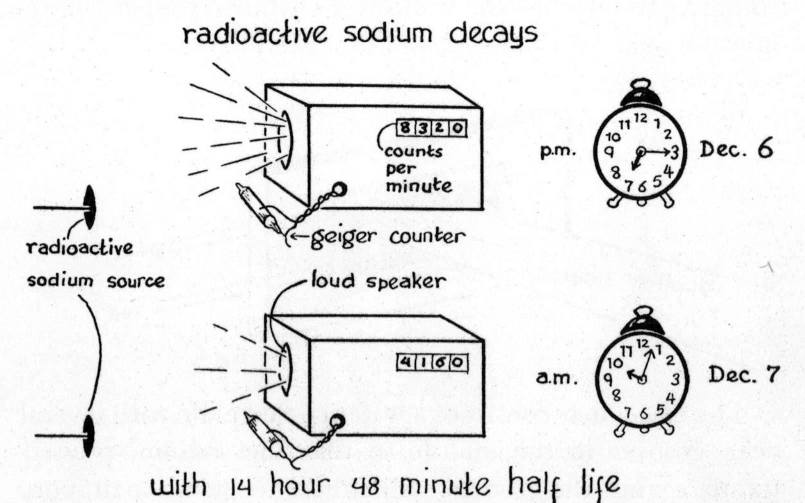

counter go crazy. Geiger counters can sometimes count as many as 20,000 particles a minute; if the particles come much faster than that, the counter is unable to cope with them. Often the radioactive sample gives off particles faster than they can be recorded in the meter. Then the sample must either be kept at a distance from the meter so that only a small fraction of the counts are recorded, or else must be put aside until the radioactivity has decayed to a value that can be measured. The loud speaker clicks as each particle passes through the counter tube; as the source is brought closer the single clicks degenerate into a low rumble. The particles emitted from the sample are counted at different intervals during its half-life, and the results of these counts are plotted on a graph. The rate of emission of particles at any time can be seen at a glance from the graph: the time required for the initial rate to diminish by half gives the characteristic half-life of the element, for sodium just under fifteen hours.

The Geiger counter is not sensitive enough to tell what sort of particles are produced by the sodium radioactivity. Though it can feel the particles it can not see them, so a single Geiger counter can not discriminate between a positron and an electron. However, a cloud chamber in a magnetic field can. The curvature of the tracks of the particles shows immediately whether they are positive or negative: the cloud chamber shows that the radioactive sodium disintegrates with the emission of an electron.

Although the cyclotron is pre-eminent in the formation of sources of artificial radioactivity, it is not the best machine to use in determining the nature of the process which makes the sodium radioactive. With sodium made radioactive from a cyclotron, it is easily possible to measure the radioactivity of the sodium after bombardment, but it is difficult to identify the process that occurred when the deuteron hit the sodium. The beam of deuterons is so intense, and the stray radiation of neutrons is so great around the cyclotron, that it would be almost impossible to use a cloud chamber at the cyclotron target to picture what happens when the deuteron meets the sodium. The voltage doubler and the Van de Graaff generators have less stray radiation, and further they produce beams of particles whose energy varies within narrow limits and can easily be measured. Part of the beam from a Van de Graaff generator is led into a cloud chamber through a thin window. Inside the chamber the beam could fall on the sodium target. With this arrangement the tracks of the particles that take part in the reaction can be photographed and measured.

Hundreds of photographs are taken in the cloud chamber. Afterwards, on reprojecting the photographs, the lengths of path of the particles are carefully measured. Then the particle given off after the deuteron has entered the sodium nucleus can be identified as a proton. With this information it is possible to write an equation showing what has happened when the sodium nucleus has been bombarded by a deuteron and given off a proton, resulting in the capture of a neutron.

$$_{11}Na^{23} + {}_1H^2 = {}_{11}Na^{24} + {}_1H^1$$

This equation, the common language of nuclear physics, signifies that a sodium atom of atomic number 11 and atomic mass 23 has been bombarded by a deuteron of number 1 and mass 2. The result on the other side of the equal sign is a sodium isotope of the same number, but heavier by one unit corresponding to the capture of a neutron, plus a proton of charge 1 and mass 1. The atomic number is usually shown by a pre-subscript, and the atomic mass by a post-superscript.

The radioactivity of the $_{11}Na^{24}$, the sodium that was observed by the Geiger counter after the target was removed from the cyclotron, can also be represented in a similar equation.

$$_{11}Na^{24} = {}_{12}Mg^{24} + e^-$$

The $_{11}Na^{24}$ disintegrates into $_{12}Mg^{24}$ with the emission of an electron. The atomic mass is the same because radioactivity with the emission of an electron means conversion of a nuclear neutron into a nuclear proton, both of which have practically equivalent mass. The atomic number has increased from 11 to 12 with consequent change of the atom from sodium to magnesium because the neutron-proton conversion in the nucleus means the gain of a single nuclear charge, one step upwards in the atomic number scale.

With cloud chamber and Van de Graaff generator, with

Geiger counter and cyclotron, it is possible to find the reactions responsible for nuclear changes. These reactions, and the energy changes that go with them, are the heart of nuclear physics. Upon this experimental basis new theories can be devised, and once devised, the theories can be put to test with further experiment. Before he can understand what happens in the nucleus the scientist must be able to describe the phenomena that accompany nuclear changes. He must have instruments to bring about the changes, and he must have instruments to measure the changes he has brought about. To understand the nucleus the scientist must be able to see inside it. The physicist can not form any adequate theory of the ultimate nature of matter without experimental evidence to support his findings.

CHAPTER 15

MEDICINE

In 1896 when Becquerel discovered radioactivity, he did more than uncover a fundamental fact of the highest importance in physics. The discovery of radium marked a new milestone in the progress of medicine. Its therapeutic value is unquestioned today; indeed the rays that Becquerel discovered have been of the highest importance in the treatment of cancer. Just one year earlier, Röntgen had discovered the x-ray, a discovery that led indirectly to radioactivity, and directly to Moseley's great work on the atomic number. Like radium, the x-radiation is useful in cancer therapy. But its use is not confined to therapy, for it is probably more widely known from the photographs that can be taken with its aid. So important are these discoveries that there is a special branch of medicine called radiology which deals with the use of radiation in the diagnosis and treatment of disease.

More recently, within a few months of one another in 1932, came the discoveries of the neutron and artificial radioactivity. Both have contributed to nuclear physics: the neutron as a constituent of the nucleus, and artificial radioactivity in the experimental detection of the products of nuclear disintegration. It is too soon to compare them with radium and the x-ray, but these modern discoveries may have as great importance for medicine as those of Becquerel and Röntgen.

Ionisation is the clue used in detection of alpha, beta, gamma and x-rays. Furthermore, ionisation is responsible for the medical application of the radiation, for it also occurs when the rays penetrate living tissue and cells. After penetration the cells are altered: sometimes the damage is sufficient to cause death, sometimes deformity, and sometimes the cell recovers completely. The intensity of the effect depends on the intensity of the ionisation, although the exact relation is still unknown. Clinically, x-radiation is measured by the Röntgen — the *r* unit, a unit of ionisation. A thin walled ionisation chamber of standard construction is placed where it will intercept a known fraction of the x-rays, and the resultant ionisation is measured in terms of *r* units.

The neutron is unable to ionise directly, so it has recourse to a secondary particle. The protons projected so violently after neutron collision serve adequately, and the major portion of the neutron effect is due to ionisation produced by protons. Other effects of the passage of neutrons through matter play a negligible role. Measurement of neutron intensity requires a chamber with walls containing hydrogen, or another material which can translate the neutron impact into some form of measurable energy. In tissue, which is very rich in hydrogen, the impact of a beam of neutrons means the production of large numbers of densely ionising protons. Clinically, neutron intensity is measured in an ionisation chamber, the composition of whose walls is rigidly prescribed so that it shall approximate tissue as closely as possible. The numerical value of the neutron unit, the *n*, is exactly equal to that of the *r*, but since the conditions are not quite the same, it is difficult to compare the two absolutely. However, once the dimensions of a neutron ionisation chamber have been specified the *n* unit is stable and reproducible.

X-rays possess one great advantage over alpha, beta, and gamma radiation. Although alpha and beta rays are heavier, and more densely ionising than x-rays, this advantage is offset because they, and gamma rays as well, are natural products. The intensity of alpha radiation is governed by natural laws, and the alpha particles are expelled in all directions. The intensity of x-radiation, however, can be controlled by the operator of the x-ray generator, and the beam itself confined to a small area. Neutrons, produced artificially in the cyclotron, can also be controlled by the operator of the cyclotron, and a beam of neutrons may be defined almost as sharply as one of x-rays.

When fast-moving deuterons impinge on a beryllium target in a cyclotron, they produce a great many neutrons. The problem of collimating the neutrons so they emerge as a well defined beam is not a simple one. First the entire target and cyclotron is surrounded with the customary three foot thick barrier of water. Immediately adjoining the target, there is a small gap in the barrier through which the neutrons may emerge. The gap is adjustable by the insertion of other small water screens, so that the size and shape of the neutron beam may be altered as desired. Neutron radiation is not the only radiation given off by the cyclotron, so the channel and the treatment room into which the neutrons emerge are also both lined with coatings of lead. Finally, the walls of the treatment room are disguised so that the patient will not be too scared by the machine that lies in wait beyond.

The biological effect of radiation may be measured in many ways. One method is the mortality rate of some selected growing organism, like wheat seedlings. Neutron irradiation has been shown to be five times as effective as x-rays in inhibiting the normal growth of seedlings per *n* unit. A possible explanation of this may be that the ionisation produced after neutron bombardment is far more dense than that produced by x-rays, because the heavy proton projected by the neutron is especially efficient in ionising. This does not imply that the measured *r* and *n* units do not represent the same amount of ionisation; rather that the neutron-proton ionisation is more concentrated. The difference in concentration between the two radiations is so great that the ionisation caused by a neutron per inch of path is one hundred times that of the x-ray.

Before authoritative statements of the action of neutrons on man are made, the Army's World War II results must be made available to the public. In the absence of this information great care must be taken to avoid undue exposure. In 1940 it was known that neutrons were about four times as effective as x-rays in producing sterility in male mice. At that time the safe daily dose of neutrons was arbitrarily designated as one-fifth that for x-rays. From the ratios of neutron to x-ray effectiveness found from other cells and animals, it is to be expected that neutrons will be of great therapeutic value. However, until further results are known, final judgment must be suspended.

Artificial radioactive elements possess two very great advantages over the natural radioactive ones. For one thing, most of the common elements can now be made radioactive; for another, this radioactivity is short-lived enough so that it can be taken internally. Only a few years ago cases came to light of factory girls apparently doomed because of overdoses of radioactive material. Not exposed directly to radiation, they had been engaged in painting luminous watch dials. Each time a girl made a numeral she touched the brush to her lips to put a fine point on it. The amount of radium carried on the brush was infinitesimally small because there is an almost imperceptible amount of radium in luminous dials — one part in 40,000 parts of paint. Yet over the course of years the girls absorbed enough radium to produce fatal results. The important fact is that the effect is cumulative, owing to the longevity of the radium activity. At no single time did they take enough radium to harm them, but once inside the body, the radium remained, continuously giving off its dangerous radiation. Radium has a half-life of 1690 years, so it does not decay appreciably during a human lifetime. If it had a short half-life and decayed within a few days, the girls would not have been harmed because the radiation would have died down shortly after the radium entered the body.

Before it was known that radium taken internally was fatal, it had been administered as a remedy in some unfortunate cases. True, it did produce an initial effect that was encouraging, but once this had worn off the radium began its insidious attack and the treatment finally ended in the death of the patient. Radium and radium products are used in the treatment of cancer today, but the dangers are recognized. The radium is not administered internally; furthermore, once it has done its good work, it is removed. Now, with the discovery of the new artificial radioactivity this great stumbling block has been removed. Of the 92 known stable elements, 87 may be made radioactive artificially, all with half-lives that are very short in comparison with that of radium. Most of these decay so quickly that they may be taken internally with no danger of a cumulative effect like radium poisoning. The intensity of radiation from radioactive phosphorus, for example, has diminished by half in 14 days. Phosphorus occurs widely in the body, so this is especially fortunate, since 14 days is an almost ideal half-life. The phosphorus retains its activity long enough to permit ample treatment, and then gives it up before any damage is done. Unfortunately, many of the elements that seem desirable for research decay so rapidly that they can hardly be used; as though nature, perversely, had given short lives to those elements whose actions are most interesting. The carbon isotope whose half-life is 21 minutes is just on the threshold: in three hours the activity has decayed to 1/500th of its initial value.

The new radioactive elements cannot be administered just as they come from the cyclotron, or other atom smasher. First they must be purified, then synthesized into some compound which is easily taken into the body. With phosphorus, these operations can be performed leisurely, because the activity does not fall off rapidly. In the case of carbon, however, time is at a premium, and new methods of synthesis have been developed to make carbon into complex compounds with a minimum loss of time.

The most encouraging results in the application of artificial radioactive therapy have come in the treatment of leukemia. Leukemia is a fatal disease that occurs with a tremendous increase in the number of white blood cells, a disease somewhat similar to cancer, in which the number of affected cells also multiplies tremendously. No cure is known for leukemia, although some alleviation and prolongation of life results from continued use of x-rays. After a short interval, the patient can no longer be exposed to further x-ray treatment, and the disease pursues its fatal course. The advantage of artificially radioactive elements in therapy is that they behave chemically exactly as do their inert isotopes. The bone normally has a high phosphorus content, and it is to be expected that a large proportion of phosphorus taken in will be deposited in the bone. Preliminary experiments have been made with radioactive phosphorus on animals, and, as expected, a large percentage of the phosphorus was found in the bones. Since the seat of production of most of the white blood cells is the bone, radioactive phosphorus offers great advantages in treatment, since the radioactivity can be applied just where it is most desired. In one recent case, a leukemia patient had been kept alive, after x-ray treatment could no longer be applied, only by the use of blood transfusions. When a phosphorus compound, made radioactive by the Harvard cyclotron, was injected, there was an immediate sharp decrease in the number of white blood cells. As a result, thc patient felt so much better that he went out and enjoyed himself for the first time in several months. It is still too soon to draw definite conclusions, but there can be little doubt that radioactive phosphorus offers a new and important tool in the treatment of leukemia.

Artificial radioactivity has another application in biology only indirectly related to its use in therapy. As with lead and radium D, small quantities of a radioactive element can be used to trace large amounts of its inactive isotope. Once infected, wherever the inactive element goes, it takes its radioactive partner. A radioactive atom does not know when it is going to disintegrate: and until it does it behaves just as an ordinary stable isotope. Only in the instant of disintegration is the radioactive atom set apart. Consequently, in the body as in the test-tube, the radioactive element acts as a tracer in the detection of quantities so small as to defy analysis.

Inside the body many complex chemical changes take place on the material that is taken in. Ordinary methods of analysis fail to show just what happens to a particular compound after it has entered the body. Although as much of the same compound may be excreted as taken in, there is no guarantee that the original material was not used to fill some particular need in the body, and the amount given off formed in an entirely unconnected process. Using artificial radioactivity, this and many similar problems may be solved. With a Geiger counter the radioactive fingerprints of the original mixture may be detected at once.

In the application of these new discoveries to medical research, there is a valid opportunity for collaboration of scientists working in many different fields. No single scientist will suffice. The physicist contributes his knowledge of the production and detection of the radioactive element; the chemist, the synthesis of the desired compound. The biologist fuses these contributions in carrying out the research. Each of the people collaborating brings his own knowledge to bear on the problem which gains by the fresh approach of men who are skilled in different fields. It has been said that the sciences have been growing apart and have become increasingly narrow. On the contrary, here scientists may come together in close collaboration for the solution of problems vital to all.

CHAPTER 16

ATOMIC POWER

HARD upon the heels of the first report of the fission of uranium, came scores of scientific papers. Physicists all over the world were frantically trying to learn more about this revolutionary process. Natural curiosity was a powerful stimulus. To this was added the thrill of doing research in an expanding field, with the ever-present chance of discovery. Uranium fission had opened up a new continent to physicists and everywhere explorers were marking out its most important features.

It soon developed that uranium fission came from slow neutrons as well as fast, and also that the fission yield from slow neutrons was very high. The explanation for this unexpected result was first put forward theoretically by Bohr, in collaboration with a former student. In the years since Bohr had first postulated the orbital theory to account for the behaviour of electrons on Rutherford's model of the nucleus atom, he had not been idle. The same great name re-enters our story some twenty-five years after its first appearance; Bohr was still labouring to understand the nucleus. In February, 1939, Bohr suggested that the slow neutron effect was due to a rare isotope of uranium—uranium 235. In 1940, a small amount of this isotope was separated in a mass-spectrograph. Experiments confirmed the theory that uranium 235 was indeed responsible for the slow neutron effect.

A general index of liability to fission is given by the ratio of the square of the atomic number to the isotopic weight. This index is high for uranium 235, a little higher, in fact, than it is for U 238. Secondly, a particular criterion is given by the number of neutrons in the nucleus. This number can be found by subtracting from the mass number, 235, which is the total number of all the protons and neutrons in the nucleus, the atomic number 92, which is the number of protons alone. When the neutron number is odd, a great deal of energy is released inside the nucleus when a new neutron arrives to make a pair with the odd one. As a result of this excess energy an odd neutron nucleus is easily fissionable. Uranium 235, present in ordinary uranium ores only to 0.7 per cent, satisfies both conditions.

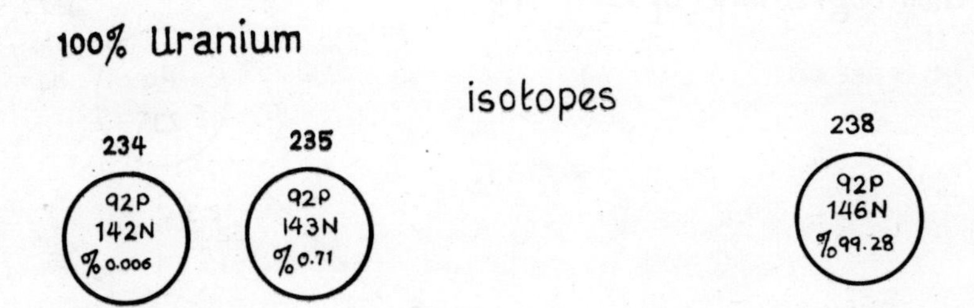

The discovery of uranium fission upset the whole carefully contrived scheme of Fermi's trans-uranic elements. These were shown to be largely fission products. However, in 1937, Hahn, Meitner, and Strassmann had shown that bombardment of uranium with neutrons produced a radioactive isotope of uranium, uranium 239, which gave off electrons with a half-life of twenty-three minutes. Loss of an electron means that inside the nucleus one neutron has turned into a proton; the atomic number has consequently risen from 92 to 93, but the mass number has not changed. A careful series of observations in the late spring of 1940 confirmed the existence of this new element, now called neptunium, and showed that it was also radioactive. Neptunium itself decayed with a half-life of 2.3 days and emitted still another electron to form a second new element, with an atomic number of 94, now called plutonium. This new element was expected to disintegrate with the emission of an alpha particle. The alpha particle has since been found; the half-life of plutonium is so long that there is no appreciable loss by radioactive decay.

One further important observation was published. In addition to the highly energetic heavy fragments thrown off in fission, neutrons were emitted. The number was indeterminate, with experimental results varying from about one to three neutrons emitted per fission. At first even the

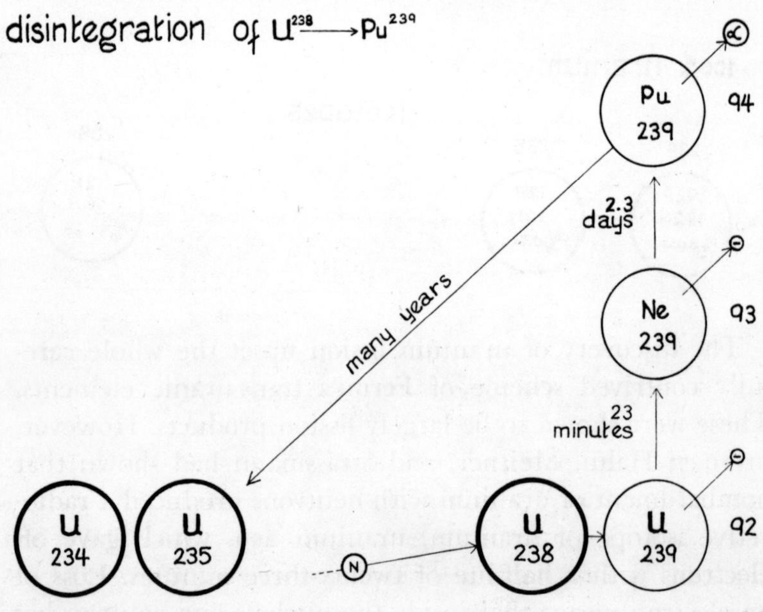

mechanism was not clearly understood. No one could definitely state whether the neutrons were emitted at the instant of fission, or were given off by the fragments later. At the time, the nature of the process was not the most arresting problem. The mere fact that a reaction caused by a single neutron could liberate great energy, and at the same time produce at least one new neutron, lent substance for the first time to the Sunday supplement's favorite stories about atomic energy. Hitherto the liberated energy per disintegration had been great, though puny in comparison with fission's 200,000,000 electron volts. But, the atom was very small, and many of the bombarding particles passed right through without penetrating a nucleus; only an infinitesimal number of nuclei were ever disintegrated. Consequently the total amount of energy produced was woefully small.

The prospect of new neutrons produced by the bombarding neutron changed that reasoning. For if one neutron produced, say, two, and each of these produced two more, fission would provide its own source of particles. And each time one neutron produced two, it would also cause nuclear fission with its attendant release of about 200,000,000

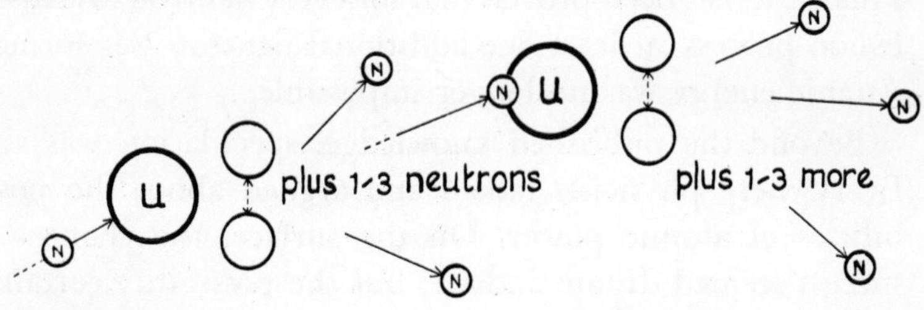

neutron capture leads to fission and more neutrons

electron volts. A host of neutrons accompanied by a great release of energy could grow from a single bombarding particle. The discovery of fission had revolutionised all our thinking about atomic power.

In the process of fission, uranium breaks up into barium and krypton, or other similar pairs of elements. When this process occurs the total weight of all the particles produced, including the weight of any neutrons thrown off, is less than the weight of uranium by about 0.2 of a mass unit. This corresponds to about one-fifth of a neutron or one-tenth of one per cent of the uranium mass. As has been shown in other nuclear reactions, mass lost in these reactions reappears as energy. Two-tenths of a neutron is roughly the equivalent of 200,000,000 electron volts. All the atoms in one kilogram of uranium in simultaneous fission would give off energy equivalent to that released in the explosion of 20,000 tons of TNT.

Broadly, this was the state of our published knowledge in the summer of 1940. Uranium fission had been discovered. Theory had predicted, and experiment confirmed, that the isotope, uranium 235, was peculiarly sensitive to fission, so much so that it only required slow neutrons to do the trick. Two trans-uranic elements, neptunium and plutonium, had been further investigated, and their position in the periodic table established with reasonable certainty. Finally, it had been proved that for every neutron lost in the fission process, at least one additional neutron was formed. Atomic energy was no longer impossible.

Beyond the published knowledge, speculation was rife. Everywhere physicists talked and argued about the possibilities of atomic power. On the surface, the chances of success seemed distant indeed; but the possibility certainly existed. Even a sober scientific review, summing up the published work at the end of 1939, stated in measured terms that "For the first time it seems there is some reasonable possibility of utilising the enormous nuclear energy of heavy atoms. If later accurate measurements of . . . the number of secondary neutrons show this to be correct the practical difficulties can undoubtedly be overcome in time."

The realisation of the potentialities of atomic power did not lag behind the discovery. In March of 1939, Fermi had discussed with the Navy the use of the atom as a weapon of war. The Navy expressed interest, and asked to be kept informed. In the fall a second attempt was made, this time an approach to President Roosevelt, supported by a letter from Einstein. The President set up a committee, and the government began to take active interest in the work. It had supported the work by a small grant of $6,000 in February of 1940. But the first real allocation came in November of 1940; $40,000 was for a year's work, on a contract given to Columbia University by the National Defense Research Council. It seems peculiarly significant that the subject was first discussed with the United States government by Fermi, an Italian who had fled from fascism in his native country. From the historical account of those early days, it is apparent that much of the driving force in this development came from the Europeans now resident in this country.

Six thousand dollars is a very small sum indeed for research on so vast a problem. Perhaps it didn't seem so to physicists in 1940, accustomed as they were to the paltry sums available for university research. Forty thousand dollars is not much more—but, after that small start, the government continually supported the work, with grants which increased as the significance and importance of the undertaking became more apparent. The staggering total of $2,000,000,000 for research and production is proof enough.

The National Defense Research Council, which gave the first contract to Columbia, was a government-run body which directed and supported the scientific work in this country. The organization was directed by a group of civilian scientists. When the Office of Scientific Research and Development, headed by Dr. Vannevar Bush, was founded, it incorporated NDRC as the supervisory arm for physical and chemical research. The NDRC gave contracts to universities and firms, under the terms of which the contractor agreed to perform certain experiments. Originally these contracts went to the universities whose staffs were carrying out the experiments. When the time came to integrate and centralize the work, the scientists had to move with their jobs. Scientifically, the history of this project was as continuous as any scientific job can be. Geographically and organisationally, it was extraordinarily discontinuous.

Before any progress could be made in evaluating the speculations of the scientific world, it was necessary to back them up with experimentally determined facts. The first thing to prove was that a chain reaction would work.

The fact that more than one new neutron was produced for each bombarding neutron was an important preliminary. It remained to be shown that these additional neutrons would themselves be effective in disintegrating further nuclei. This problem is not easy. There are a number of competing fates which await the neutron wandering through a lump of uranium. First, if the lump is small, the neutron may escape through the surface into the atmosphere outside. This can be minimized only by making the amount of uranium very large. Second, the neutron may be captured by impurities in the uranium. Some of these impurities have a probability of neutron capture vastly in excess of that of uranium. Third, the neutron may be captured by uranium in a reaction which does not produce fission. It is this process which occurs when a neutron is captured by uranium 238 to produce U 239, leading to the end-product plutonium. Only a neutron, not lost to any of these competitive processes, is available to cause fission of another uranium atom, produce more neutrons, and thus carry on the chain.

It was already known that the highest yield of fission came from bombardment of uranium 235 by slow neutrons. Consequently slow neutrons were used in the first serious attempt to produce a chain reaction. As has been discussed, the standard method of slowing down neutrons is to send them through a large amount of water, paraffin, or other material containing hydrogen. When a neutron hits a light nucleus, the energy is split between the two particles in inverse proportion to their mass.

To be effective, the slowing down material, or moderator, should not absorb neutrons from the limited supply. Of the light elements, which make the best moderators, heavy hydrogen, beryllium, and carbon are best. Ordinary hydrogen is unsuitable because it captures neutrons to form heavy hydrogen. A high degree of purity is demanded of the moderator, for impurities capture neutrons. In addition to all these requirements, the moderator should be available in large quantities in a form which is readily handled. Heavy hydrogen did not exist in great quantities. Beryllium of high purity was rare. Carbon was available, and methods could be found to produce enough pure carbon in the form of graphite for tests. As a result carbon was chosen, not necessarily because it was scientifically best, but because it alone, of the satisfactory substances, gave promise of being available.

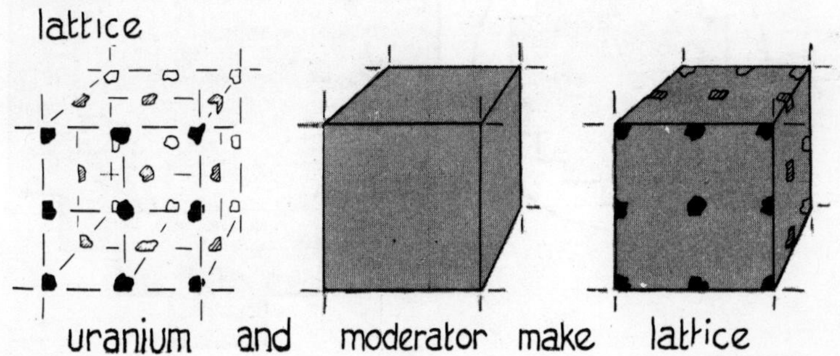

Careful consideration of the method of mixing carbon with uranium soon showed that a lattice arrangement would be better than a homogeneous mixture. The reasoning was this: upon fission fast neutrons were released. For the greatest effectiveness in producing further fissions they had to be slowed down. But before they reached a slow enough speed to be effective in producing U 235 fission they passed through a dangerous region—a speed corresponding to an energy of about twenty-five electron volts. Uranium 238 has a very high probability of capturing twenty-five volt neutrons to form U 239. But by carefully spacing the uranium in a well-chosen lattice, with the interstices filled with moderator and by choosing the distance from one uranium mass to another this danger could be made very small. For if the neutron once escaped from the uranium mass in which it was formed, it would have to travel far enough through the carbon moderator to slow it down well below the twenty-five volt region. Thus the neutron loss to uranium 238 could be reduced, and the number of free neutrons available to cause fission enhanced.

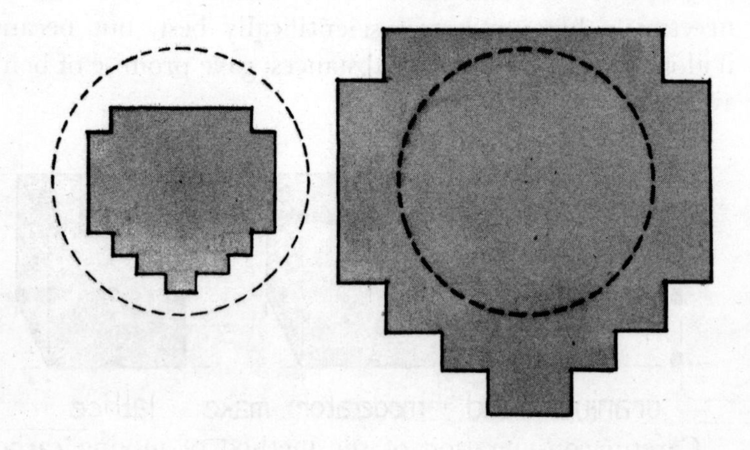

With a careful choice of moderator, with adequate purity of materials, and with a lattice structure, the chance of neutron capture by non-fission processes was certainly minimized. But there still remained the possibility of loss to the surrounding atmosphere. For any given surface area a sphere has the greatest volume. Since neutrons are produced throughout the volume of the material, and since they can only be lost through the surface, the optimum shape is spherical. Having once determined shape, size becomes important. Enough neutrons must be produced so that the number lost to the atmosphere is negligible. This condition immediately sets a lower limit to the size of the experiment. Once one has adjusted all the conditions inside the material to their best value, more neutrons can be made available only by an increase in size. For given conditions inside, a certain critical size must be exceeded before the chain reaction can go. If the pile, as these experimental lattices were called, is smaller than the critical size, the number of neutrons lost to the outside makes the reaction impossible. As soon as the pile exceeds that critical size, a chain reaction is possible. Furthermore the reaction needs no detonator since there are enough stray neutrons floating about in the atmosphere to initiate the reaction. These neutrons can be produced by cosmic rays, by the secondary effects from normal radioactive disintegration of uranium, or by spontaneous fission.

All during 1941, experiments were carried out in laboratories throughout the country. Measurements were taken—numbers were found, and the processes of capture and absorption of neutrons were examined in great detail. In July of 1941 at Columbia University, the first lattice structure of graphite and uranium was set up. This lattice was a cube about eight feet on each side. It contained about seven tons of a commercial grade of uranium oxide.

The easiest way to describe the operation of a lattice is to characterize it by its multiplication factor, 'k.' The necessary condition for a chain reaction is that each incoming neutron produces slightly more than one new neutron. k is the multiplication factor for the incident neutron. If, throughout the whole pile, one neutron is produced per incident neutron, k is 1.0. If, on the average, only one-half a neutron is produced, k is 0.5; if two are produced, k is 2.0. The critical condition for a chain reaction is that k be at least unity. This is an exact way of stating that the reaction will only proceed if, after subtracting all the neutrons that are lost to the competing reactions, one new neutron is produced by each bombarding neutron. In the first lattice at Columbia, this condition was not met. Mathematically it is possible to extrapolate the value of k obtained with any pile to the value that k would have if the pile were of infinite size. In an infinite pile no neutrons can be lost to the atmosphere outside. With the first lattice at Columbia it was found that the k for infinite size was only 0.87. With these impure materials the reaction would not go.

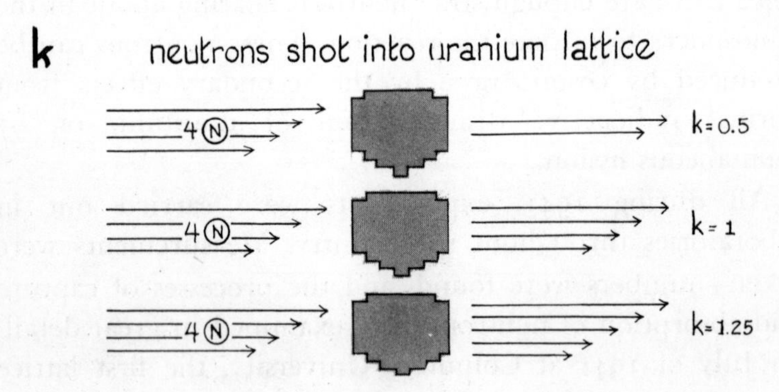

some are captured or stray but fission forms many new neutrons

In January, 1942, when it was decided to concentrate much of this experimental work at one place, the "Metallurgical Laboratory" was established at the University of Chicago. The name was chosen so that it would have no discernible connection with the atomic energy project. One of the immediate objectives of this laboratory was to set up a natural uranium pile of sufficient size and purity so that the chain reaction would work. The Columbia pile had failed because the materials were impure, and it was necessary to arrange for purification of the uranium and carbon before seriously beginning construction of the Chicago pile.

At that time, only a few pounds of uranium metal existed in the United States, and of that only a few grams were relatively pure. The material that had been used at Columbia was uranium oxide containing an appreciable percentage of impurities. Many months of 1942 were consumed before a satisfactory supply of purified uranium was attained. It was only in the fall that enough purified uranium, uranium oxide, and graphite were assembled to make the construction of a pile feasible.

But the physicists were not idle during this period. In one set of experiments they investigated the emission of delayed neutrons. It had been observed and, in fact, published that a small percentage of neutrons were emitted after the fission was over. Investigation and remeasurement showed that this fraction was about one per cent. During the course of the work on the atomic project old measurements were made over again with higher precision in order to make sure that the most accurate constants served as a basis for engineering processes. Of the one per cent of delayed neutrons, some were emitted only a few seconds after fission, while a few stragglers delayed as long as a minute.

The importance of delayed neutrons was that they provided a control for the chain reaction. k could always be made smaller by the introduction of neutron absorbing material into the pile. Cadmium is a very efficient neutron absorber, and consequently cadmium rods were inserted into the pile whenever it was necessary to suck neutrons out. With the use of cadmium rods, k could be set at a value so that, without the contribution of the delayed neutrons, the chain reaction would not take place. With the delayed neutrons, k would be slightly greater than unity, and the reaction would work. The delayed neutron contribution gave a period of grace lasting up to a minute, in which the reaction could be controlled, if it showed any signs of being too active. In practice, a cadmium rod, with its depth of penetration into the pile governed automatically by an ionisation chamber in the pile, provided safe and effective operation at any specified power level.

In November, 1942, construction of a new pile began in a squash court under the West Stands of Stagg Field. Purified material was at hand, and calculation indicated that a k several per cent greater than unity should be realised. There still was not enough pure uranium to do the whole job, and the lattice was padded with uranium oxide. The pure metal was reserved for the centre where the neutron density was highest.

It was planned to make the pile approximately spherical. The graphite was cut in bricks, and carefully placed in position. Every other layer included lumps of uranium at the corners of squares. As new layers were added, holes were left for cadmium rods, ionisation gauges, and other recording instruments. Each day the pile grew and measurements were taken to check that its performance agreed with calculation. For safety, the cadmium rods, normally in the retard position, were removed only once a day for these necessary measurements. In the words of the official report, "This was fortunate since the approach to critical condition was found to occur at an earlier stage of assembly than had been anticipated." Only three-quarters of the pile was completed when the critical size was reached. As a result, the final structure, containing six tons of pure uranium, looked less like a sphere than a gigantic door-knob.

Finally, on December 2, 1942, the controls were adjusted and the pile was allowed to operate. It produced energy—one-half of a watt. Here was the first proof that the calculations, that the months of work, were justified. Here was a chain reaction which produced energy from the atomic nucleus. This magnificent achievement is not to be measured by the amount of energy produced; the achievement is that, on December 2, 1942, man first showed that nuclear power could be tapped and tamed.

CHAPTER 17

URANIUM 235 AND PLUTONIUM

DRIVEN by the urgency of war, there was no time to complete one experiment before launching another. Many possible processes had to be explored simultaneously, as the greatest precaution lest the enemy arrive at the answer before us. There was reason to believe that he was working on the same problem. In 1940 it had been reported that a large section of the Kaiser Wilhelm Institute in Berlin was working on uranium. Later, uncertainty about the German progress must have extended into the top military command, for, in the words of Mr. Winston Churchill, "In the winter of 1942-43 most gallant attacks were made in Norway on two occasions by small parties of volunteers from the British Commandos and Norwegian forces, at very heavy loss of life, upon stores of what is called 'heavy water,' an element in one of the possible processes. The second of these two attacks was completely successful."

A certain prerequisite for any bomb at all was a supply of ready materials. All during the time that work was proceeding on the chain reaction at Chicago, others were busy with the problem of separation of uranium 235. This isotope, so particularly suited for fission, would clearly be of great use either for the construction of smaller piles to give atomic power, or for the actual construction of a bomb. An airborne bomb, with its stringent restriction on size, would certainly require the most fissionable material.

In the exciting days that followed the realization of the importance of uranium 235, many efforts were made to separate it from the much more abundant uranium 238.

Such a process cannot be carried out by simple chemical means because chemically all isotopes behave almost identically. The chemical properties of an element are largely determined by the number of electrons in the atom. This number is equal to the nuclear charge, that is, to the atomic number. All isotopes possess identical atomic number; so separation requires a process dependent primarily on the mass of the isotope.

The mass difference between the two most abundant isotopes in hydrogen is only one mass unit. However this represents one hundred per cent increase in weight. In uranium, the difference between the two most abundant isotopes, 238 and 235, is 3 mass units, but this represents only about one per cent difference in weight. The percentage difference in weight in hydrogen is important enough that it affects even the chemical properties of the two isotopes so that chemical reactions can be used to extract heavy hydrogen from ordinary hydrogen. Such a chemical method was used in one of the schemes for the concentration of deuterium that sprang up when it seemed that deuterium would be required as a moderator.

The one per cent difference in weight made it difficult to separate uranium 235. Many ingenious schemes were proposed, and several of these were carried through the pilot stage into semi-production. Of these, only two schemes finally went into major production. Neither of these depended on novel principles, and hence could be put into production with the smallest danger of major unexpected difficulties.

The first of these schemes, gaseous diffusion, was originally suggested for separation of gases in 1896. This plan depends on the velocity of the individual gas molecules. All the molecules in a gas are constantly in motion, darting back and forth. It can be shown that at any given temperature the molecules of lighter gases travel faster than those of heavier ones. In the case of isotopes, the difference in average speed is very small because it depends on the square root of the molecular weight. The gas used, uranium hexa-fluoride, has molecular weights of 349 and 352, depending on the uranium isotope—fluorine has no isotopes. If the uranium hexa-fluoride gas is sucked through a porous barrier, through which it passes with some difficulty, the faster molecules will get through sooner. But the difference in speed is so small that the isotope separation in any single stage is very slight indeed, and it is necessary to repeat the process many times.

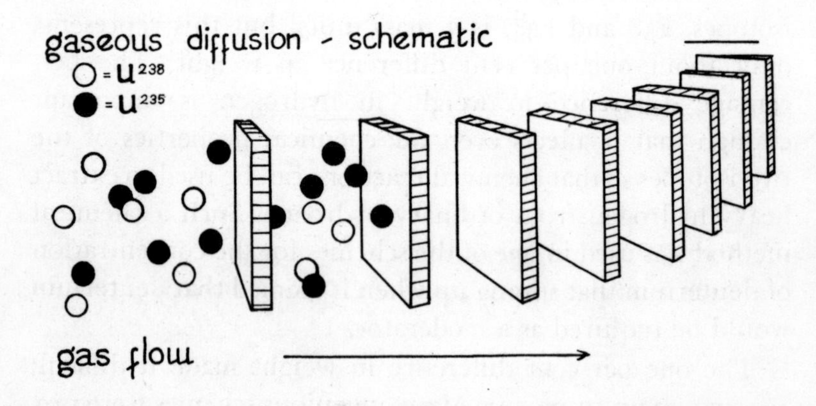

Consequently, translation of this scheme into engineering reality required a tremendous plant, much ingenuity, and a great deal of patience. To supervise the atomic bomb project, the Army in 1942 had activated a new engineering district, called Manhattan District. Major General L. R. Groves, whom the Secretary of War chose to head the Manhattan District, inspected a seventy-square-mile tract at Oak Ridge in the Tennessee Valley, and approved its acquisition as the site for the contemplated plant. This vast Tennessee organization was called the Clinton Engineer Works.

Work was begun on the gaseous diffusion plant in the summer of 1943. The many stages necessary to achieve any appreciable separation of the isotopes demanded a huge plant if uranium 235 was to be produced in the amounts required. The problem of devising the acres of barrier through which the gas would be sucked was very difficult to solve, and the final solution did not come until after work was well advanced on the plant. Thousands of pumps were required to suck the gas through the barriers, and to recompress it for further stages of the process. Even the pumps had to be of a new design, because, as the concentration of uranium 235 in the gas increased, the material became so valuable that loss had to be avoided at all costs. The job was not made any easier by the condition of the site itself. Clinton Engineer Works at Oak Ridge, Tennessee was remarkable for its "seas of mud, clouds of dust, and general turmoil." Despite all these problems, the plant was operated successfully before the summer of 1945.

The electromagnetic separation, the other method in mass production, depends on the same processes that were put to such good use by Aston in his work on isotope detection after World War I. In a uniform magnetic field, positive ions will travel in a circle provided they all enter the field with the same velocity, and they all have the same mass. If the mass is different, the radius of the circle will be different; in fact, the radius of the circle is directly proportional to the mass of the particle. This provides a better separation factor than the gaseous diffusion process, in which the effect is proportional only to the square root of the mass.

Armed with the idea of an electromagnetic separator, Lawrence and his group at the University of California took the 37-inch cyclotron apart to obtain the necessary magnet. Thereupon the device was called a "calutron" from California University cyclotron. The fact that many people had prophesied that the idea was impossible because of the numerous technical difficulties must have been a tremendous incentive to the group. They shot a beam of ions into a large vacuum tank placed between the poles of the magnet—it is quite possible that they adopted the cyclotron tank itself. As soon as the ions entered the magnetic field, their path was curved into a semicircle. A catcher was placed at the other end of the tank, its spacing carefully arranged so that it would collect the uranium 235 ions, and not the heavier ones. The major problems, concerned primarily with the

electromagnetic separation - schematic

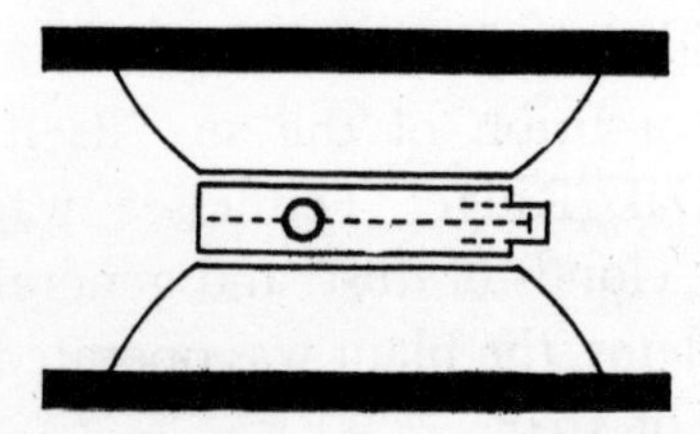

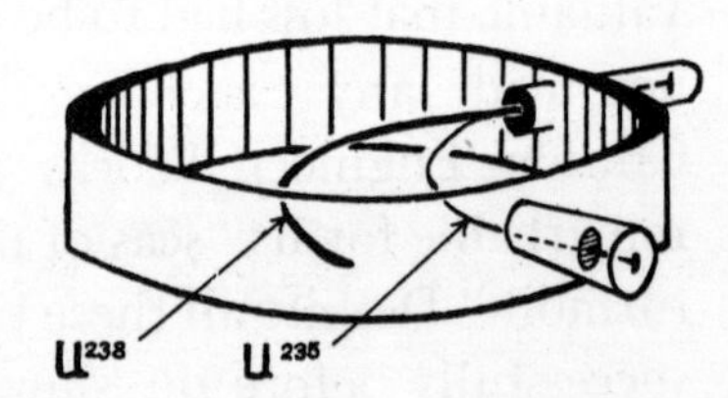

production of an intense beam of ions, were finally solved and on December 6, 1941 Lawrence reported that he could deposit one microgram of relatively pure uranium 235 in one hour.

Further research was required to attain a process satisfactory for large-scale production. Work had begun before the war on the construction of a giant cyclotron at Berkeley. Construction of the magnet, with a pole diameter of 184 inches, and a six-foot gap between the pole pieces, had been suspended on account of the war. Heartened by the results obtained in December the necessary priorities for the completion of this magnet were granted. The use of the great magnet provided more experience, the process was improved, and the men working on the project acquired a fund of empirical knowledge. Yields of the separated isotope constantly increased. As a result, General Groves authorized in November, 1942, the construction of a production plant to be located at the Clinton Engineer Works.

The first series of electromagnetic separators was ready for operation in November of the next year. After that, for nearly a year, it was the only plant in operation. The pressure for increased output was tremendous, and the California group was continually at work devising improvements. The most notable increase in yield came from a decision to start the electromagnetic process with uranium which had been previously enriched so that it contained a much higher proportion of uranium 235. Niels Bohr has stated in a recent interview after his return to Copenhagen that the United States is producing a total of three kilograms of uranium 235 per day. In four years we have achieved an increase in production almost one billion fold.

To a physicist, however, the production of uranium 235 is dwarfed by the fascination of the true story of the plutonium plants. On the face of it no madder venture has ever been coldly planned by scientists of a civilised nation. A bald statement of facts is staggering. Only when one is blinded by knowledge of partial achievement of the end result, can one accept the undertaking as being even remotely sensible. Plutonium is an element unknown on the earth. By the end of 1942, we had manufactured in this country 500/millionths of a gram of this element. Thereupon, in January of 1943 we decided to go into production, and started to build a plant with an output on the order of 1,000,000,000 watts to produce about one thousand grams of the substance a day. As if to make the problem more interesting, the plant gave off radiation of a magnitude hitherto unknown on earth. Those are the bare bones of the problem.

Good ideas always occur in many places simultaneously. Thus there are many scientists who independently suggested the production of plutonium in piles. Some of the vast number of neutrons that are available in a pile would surely be captured by uranium 238 to form uranium 239. By natural processes this isotope would decay with the formation of plutonium. This new element could be separated from uranium by normal chemical means. Like uranium 235, plutonium 239 has an odd neutron number. The ratio of its atomic number squared to its mass number is even higher than that of uranium 235. Consequently this new element can be expected to be more easily fissionable than uranium 235.

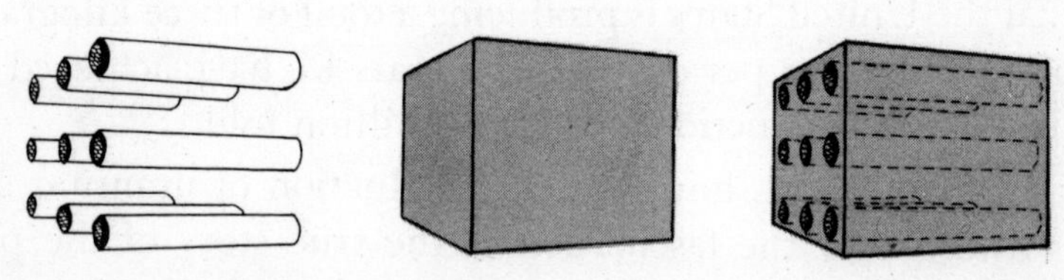

With the decision to go into large-scale production of plutonium came many new problems. Uranium could no longer be imbedded in static lumps; it had to flow through the pile, as the neutrons worked to produce plutonium. New material had to be fed into the pile as the processed uranium was taken away for chemical separation. Dissipation of 1,000,000 kilowatts required a magnificent cooling system. Both of these conditions could be satisfied with an arrangement in which tubes filled with uranium passed right through the lattice. With suitable isolation and protection of the uranium, the cooling material could be pumped through the same tubes. New material could be inserted in one end of the tube, and the processed material pushed out the other. After much further research this new lattice arrangement was shown to be satisfactory for a working pile.

Originally, the Clinton Engineer Works in Tennessee had been chosen as the site for all the work. But, upon reconsideration of the problems and dangers, General Groves decided that Clinton was not isolated enough. A new site, known as the Hanford Engineer Works, was chosen at Hanford in the state of Washington on the Columbia River near the Grand Coulee power line. However, construction of a small plant of about one thousand kilowatts was authorized at Clinton. This was designed not only as a pilot plant, but also to provide plutonium for research on the chemical separation problems. Because of a change in the cooling process as the Hanford plans advanced, the Clinton plant did not serve as a true pilot, though it provided the much needed plutonium.

The Columbia River, "the finest supply of pure cold river water in this country," provided the cooling. Water was pumped through the piles in aluminum tubes; aluminum was chosen because it is a low neutron absorber. Since uranium reacts with water, uranium slugs were sealed in aluminum cans. The cans were required to transmit the great heat of the process to the water flowing by so that the uranium would be satisfactorily cooled, and at the same time to keep the gaseous and other fission products from getting out. This problem, which was the very crux of the whole operation, was not satisfactorily solved until the very last moment.

Chemical separation of the plutonium from the uranium is difficult because the uranium contains only about one-tenth of one per cent of plutonium. When it emerges from the pile the slug is contaminated by a large assortment of fission products, whose elimination is not easy. The method finally used relied on successive cycles of precipitation, dissolution, oxidation, and further precipitation.

But over all these processes hung the dreadful pall of radiation. With no radiation, the job to be done was difficult enough; with radiation, it took on epic proportions. Piles of this magnitude give off radiation infinitely greater than anything experienced before. At Hanford, it was first necessary to protect the personnel from hazards. Periodic checks of white blood count became routine. Much research was carried out on the effects of radiation. Tolerances were established; instruments were invented to measure whether the tolerable radioactivity was exceeded. These included "Sneezy" which measured the radioactive dust concentration in the air, and "Pluto" which measured contamination of desks and equipment. Geiger counters were used at the exit gates to sound an alarm when anyone contaminated passed through the gates.

Other difficulties arose when the "hot" uranium slugs were taken from the pile for chemical processing. The slugs were transported under water to a series of concrete cells almost completely buried in the ground. When first the uranium was dissolved, it contained myriads of fission products, all intensely radioactive. Tall stacks were built to carry off the radioactive gases and discharge them high in the air. Although no experiments had been possible on the effect the radiation would have on the chemical processes of separation, fortunately it was found to do no harm. This whole complex of processes—dissolution, precipitation, oxidation—was completed from a distance by remote control.

Radiation of this magnitude might be expected to affect the very properties of matter. As with chemical properties no one could confirm experimentally the effect of radiation on the materials comprising the pile. Experience has now shown that the electric resistance, the elasticity, and the heat conduction of the graphite in the piles all change with exposure to such intense neutron radiation. The whole pile was enclosed in heavy concrete walls made airtight to avoid inducing radioactivity in the very air. Men could work with their hands, building the pile, testing the controls, making all the final adjustments, with no danger to health at all. But once the pile began to operate, no human could approach without fatal effects.

CHAPTER 18

THE ATOMIC BOMB

SLOW neutrons served best for a controlled reaction, as in the gigantic piles for the production of plutonium. But, for an explosive reaction, the minute fraction of a second taken to slow the neutrons down was too long; fast neutrons were required. Further research was necessary to determine the critical size for a fast neutron bomb. Initiation of the explosion at a pre-determined time was perhaps the most difficult of all the problems remaining.

To solve these problems, much of the equipment already described in this book was marshalled for the experiments under way. From time to time, many physicists had disappeared from their previous war-time pursuits, to take up residence in some unknown spot. We now know that that spot was the laboratory at Los Alamos, situated on a New Mexican mesa, twenty miles from Santa Fe. From its beginning this laboratory was directed by Professor J. R. Oppenheimer of the University of California. Oppenheimer had been a theoretical physicist with a brilliant inquiring mind. He had a peculiar power of self-absorption, and the tales of his absent-mindedness are legion. However, the mind that could solve problems in theoretical physics soon reoriented itself, and Oppenheimer dealt easily with the trying problems of administration, as well as the manifold technical ones in a laboratory set up expressly to create an atomic bomb.

Before the bomb could be engineered, accurate and reliable measurements were demanded of all the nuclear constants of the materials involved. Indeed, many of the measurements that had previously been reported in journals were made again with increased accuracy. This work required all the nuclear apparatus that could be made available. Initially, the laboratory got its start with three carloads of assorted equipment from the Princeton physics department. The Harvard cyclotron was uprooted and despatched to the project, as well as a pressure Van de Graaff generator from the University of Wisconsin. From the University of Illinois came a Cockcroft-Walton voltage doubler. All the conventional instruments for measurement must have been required in great numbers—electroscopes, ionisation chambers, Geiger counters, cloud chambers. Before the war, many of these instruments were at best makeshift, with all the peculiar quality that attaches to homemade laboratory instruments. For this project, many of them must have been engineered and turned into reliable calibrated instruments.

But more important even than instruments are the men who design and operate them. By 1944, Oppenheimer had attracted a great many keen physicists to Los Alamos. All during the period that the early work on the project was going on in this country, the British had been busy also in England and Canada. The original impetus to carry out the project had been strengthened and confirmed by British advice and counsel from the earliest days. At Los Alamos, a British delegation headed by Sir James Chadwick made many contributions to the success of the laboratory. Niels Bohr, after a desperate escape from Denmark, spent much time at Los Alamos. From many universities, American physicists came, and key men were even released from other important war work to go to Los Alamos.

One of the nuclear physics experiments of great interest and importance was measurement of the exact chance of neutron capture of uranium 238, uranium 235, and plutonium. Neutron experiments are traditionally difficult be cause the neutron, since it does not ionise directly, cannot be observed directly. Secondary neutron effects give the clue to its presence. With no ionisation it can give no tracks in the cloud chamber, nor allow any direct measurement in a Geiger counter. It is always necessary to provide some substance with which the neutron reacts and then to observe the result of this reaction. Thus a Geiger counter may be filled with boron trifluoride gas, and the particles produced when the neutron reacts with boron may be counted. Or a piece of cadmium foil may be placed in the neutron beam, and the resultant radioactivity may be measured by a counter.

Not only are neutrons difficult to detect, they are also difficult to control. Charged particles can be accelerated to definite speeds by the use of electric and magnetic fields. But the neutron, lacking charge, will not succumb to these influences. Consequently production of a beam of neutrons of a definite speed is most difficult. Certain ranges of velocities are produced naturally in some specified nuclear reactions. Here the speed of the emerging neutrons is given by the inexorable action of the laws of conservation of mass and energy. Speeds intermediate between those produced in the available reactions are much more difficult to obtain. Nonetheless, in the experimental work at Los Alamos, the probability of fission has been determined as a function of the energy of the bombarding neutron over the vast range from about zero to three million electron volts.

Since the atomic bomb depended on fast neutrons, experimental verification of the results in fast neutron fission was most desirable. One such set of experiments is described in the official report. A pile was built containing a mixture of uranium and a hydrogen moderator. It is not stated explicitly that uranium containing a higher than normal amount of uranium 235 was used; but certainly many experiments using enriched materials must have been carried out. In its original form, the pile contained enough moderator to be a slow neutron reacting pile. After the first results were obtained, it was torn down, and rebuilt with less moderator. More results were obtained, and the pile was again rebuilt containing still less moderator. This process, as it went on, approached more and more closely the conditions to be found in a bomb, when the fast neutron reaction would predominate.

For the atomic bomb, as for the pile, there is a critical size, below which the number of neutrons escaping from the material is so great that there will be no sustained reaction; above which an explosion will occur. Certainly one most important function of the new materials, plutonium and uranium 235, is to keep the critical size small. A further device to aid in this direction is a tamper, a non-absorbent envelope surrounding the bomb which reflects the neutrons back into it.

To bring about the greatest explosion, the bomb must be held together as long as possible so that the nuclear reaction will have worked on the maximum amount of material. Once the bomb has begun to disintegrate, the reaction will stop because the neutron density will become too low. So in an effective bomb there is the double problem of providing enough neutrons to make the bomb explode, and of holding the bomb together as long as possible to make the explosion as violent as possible. The tamper aids in this last, because in addition to reflecting neutrons back into the bomb, its own inertia makes it harder for the bomb to blow up.

The very nature of critical size imposes a peculiar limitation on the experiments that are possible. Normal explosives can be tested in small quantities. Not so the nuclear explosion, for it must be tested with amounts exceeding the critical size, or not at all. This imposes a heavy responsibility on the theoretical calculations in bomb research. A large group of theoretical physicists had been established at Los Alamos. As they gained experience, methods were devised to obtain closer and closer approximation to the true answer, until accurate calculations gave the critical size and much other important data.

But the major problem was detonation. The bomb had to be transported in fragments smaller than critical size, for once critical size was reached there were plenty of stray neutrons to bring about unpremeditated detonation. A large calibre gun was proposed to shoot one part of the bomb into the other for detonative assembly. This novel projectile had to travel at high speed along an accurate trajectory. For, should the bomb detonate before assembly was completed, it might go off with a fraction of the calculated energy released. Should it fail to detonate, we would present the enemy with our greatest secret, complete with a supply of the necessary material to help him in his experiments. The complexity of the problem can be gauged from the fact that three of the six divisions in the scientific organisation at Los Alamos were concerned with detonation and explosive problems.

Finally, on July 16, 1945, came the test which crowned these long years of calculation, of experiment, of manufacture. Careful though the work had been, checked and counter-checked by repeated tests, calculation, and experiment, the final result was always in doubt. The scientists and technicians at work on the bomb at a remote and isolated spot on Alamogordo Air Base must have been tense with excitement. All through the dark and dismal night, final arrangements were being completed, and everywhere, in all the groups watching, tension must have grown. The results of the experiment were dreadful enough in anticipation.

"Suddenly at 5:29:50 . . . a voice rang through the darkness, sounding as though it had come from above the clouds: 'Zero minus ten seconds!'

"A green flare flashed out through the clouds, descended slowly, opened, grew dim and vanished in the darkness.

"The voice from the clouds boomed out again: 'Zero minus three seconds!'

"Silence reigned over the desert. . . . From the east came the first faint signs of dawn.

"And just at that instant there rose from the bowels of the earth a light not of this world, the light of many suns in one.

"It was a sunrise such as the world had never seen, a great green super-sun climbing in a fraction of a second to a height of more than 8,000 feet, rising ever higher until it touched the clouds, lighting up earth and sky all around with a dreadful luminosity.

"Up it went, a great ball of fire about a mile in diameter, changing colors as it kept shooting upward, from deep purple to orange, expanding, growing bigger, rising as it was expanding, an elemental force freed from its bonds after being chained for billions of years.

"For a fleeting instant the color was unearthly green, such as one sees only in the corona of the sun during a total eclipse.

"It was as though the earth had opened and the skies had split."

With achievement, came relief. The work was done—the bomb was proved. But this first climax was not the end; it was a beginning. There is a story that goes the rounds—probably apocryphal. One of the high military officials who watched the experiment grew more and more tense as the moment grew near. Stirred by the terrible fury of the explosion he burst out, "My God, the long hairs have lost control." And so we physicists have. Not precisely in a way he feared, but in a way equally terrible.

It must be clear from all that is contained in this book that the atomic bomb is no secret. It obeys the fundamental laws of nature. The exact details of its composition, operation, and detonation are still military secrets. But these are technological problems that will yield to persistence and imagination. The great question was—would a bomb work. The answer we have demonstrated to all the world. With this knowledge, these results can be duplicated in a few years, at far less cost, by any capable group of scientists throughout the world.

Having demonstrated this fact, the physicists have indeed lost control. A few years hence, a nation, any willful nation, can destroy our major cities in a few hours. For this we have no remedy. We may indeed be able to destroy their cities afterwards, but the whole basis of our communications and our economy—that is, the heart of our ability to make war—will have been wrecked. We have proved the atomic bomb, and in so doing we have placed ourselves at the mercy of the world.

The implications of this fact are clear. Beyond all else, this country must strive to establish a peaceful concourse of nations. This fact transcends all worry about our national economy and prosperity. What is the good of a free and prosperous nation if it must exist under this new Damoclean sword?

Certain subsidiary facts appear. As a military necessity this nation has taken steps to acquire control of all American uranium deposits. If, as now seems likely, useful power can be developed from nuclear disintegration, this government will have perforce nationalised one of its major sources of power. This is but one example of the intricate inter-

Signal Corps, U. S. Army

One of the production plants at the Clinton Engineer Works.

The production areas of the Hanford Engineer Works.

Signal Corps, U. S. Army

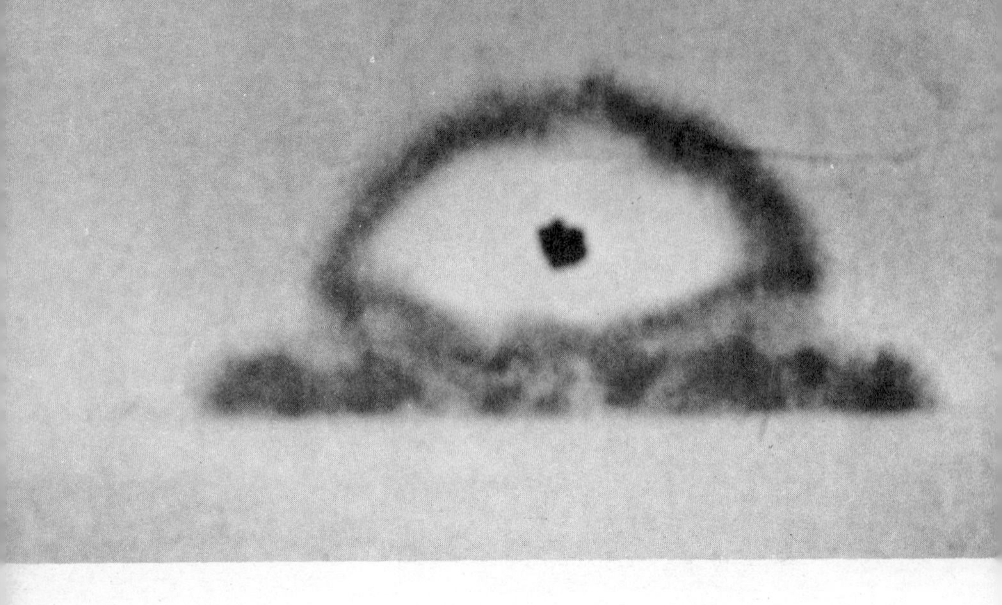

U. S. Army photo from Acme

Four pictures from a motion picture taken by the U. S. Army of the first atomic bomb explosion at Alamogordo. "The dark blotches in the early frames of the atomic bomb sequence are prints of holes in the photographic gelatin

U. S. Army photo from Acme

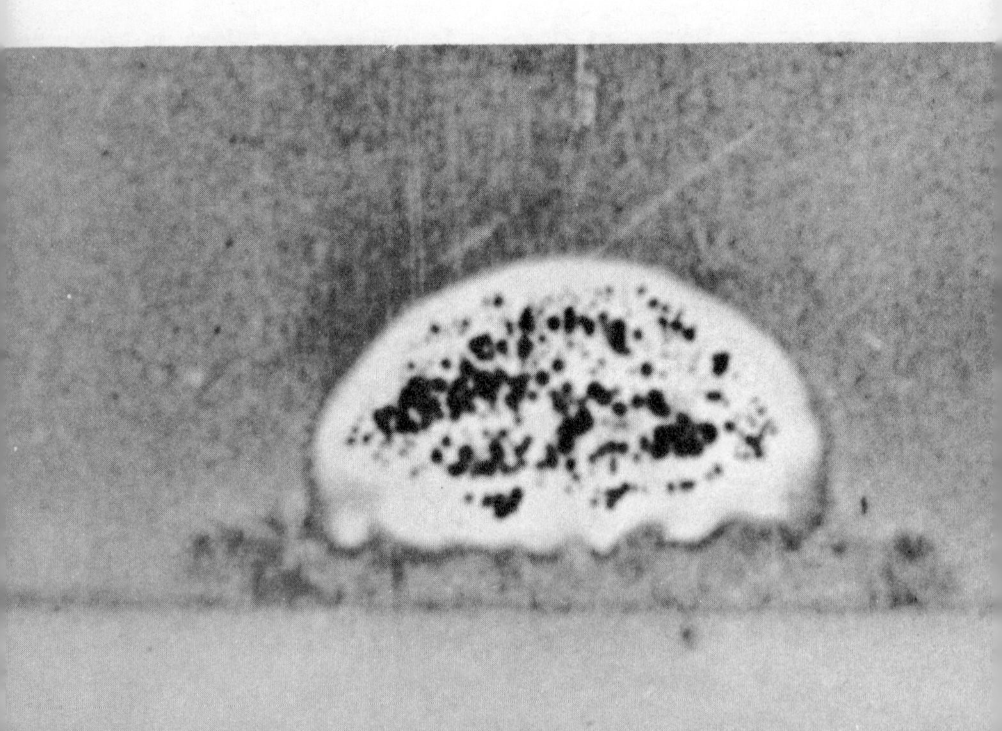

U. S. Army photo from Acme

which resulted from what was perhaps the greatest photographic over-exposure ever made in motion pictures," according to a letter in *Time Magazine* from the scientist in charge of obtaining photographic records at Los Alamos.

U. S. Army

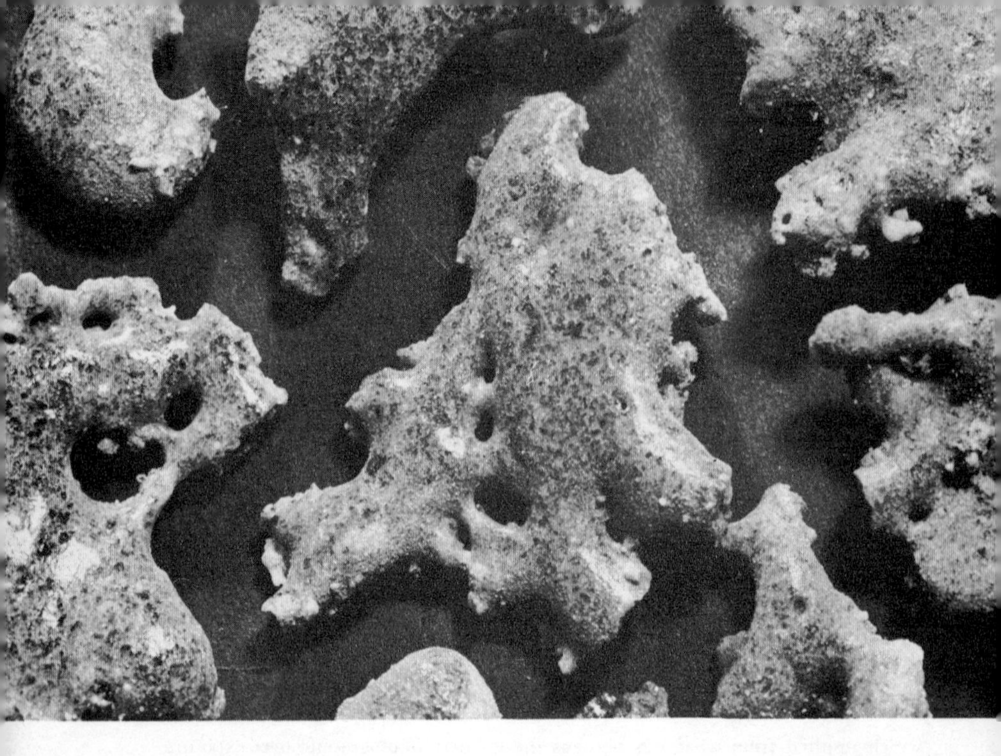

F. W. Goro for Life Magazine

Fragments of the fused sand taken from the Alamogordo site after the first atomic bomb explosion.

Close-up of a portion of the jade green fused desert sand after the atomic bomb explosion at Alamogordo. In the center can be seen the remains of a plant.

F. W. Goro for Life Magazine

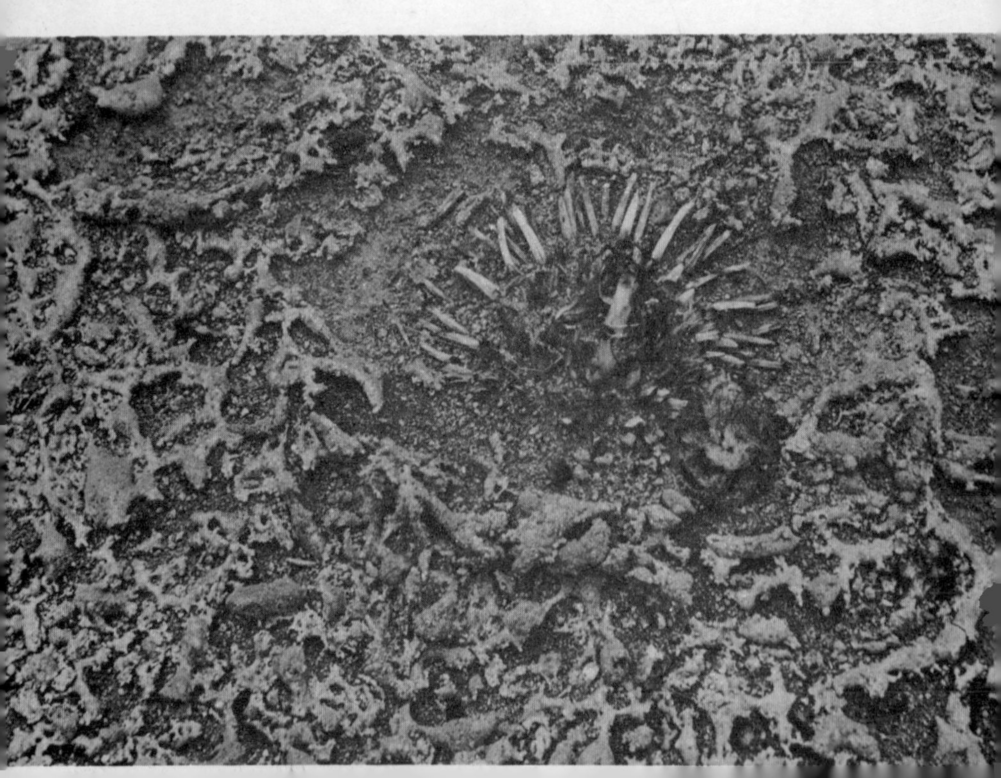

F. W. Goro for Life Magazine

Alamogordo site after the first atomic bomb explosion. The Sierra Oscura range looms in the distance. The steel tower which held the bomb was vaporized by the explosion. It stood at the junction of the roads leading to the center of the picture. Surrounding the junction is an area of jade green fused sand, which appears dark in the photograph. The white circles in the left center remain from earlier use as a conventional bombing range. A circular fence now surrounds the site.

F. W. Goro for Life Magazine

Professor J. R. Oppenheimer.

F. W. Goro for Life Magazine

Major General L. R. Groves.

mingling of this new destructive power with necessary social action. Throughout the whole fabric of the results that stem from these new discoveries, the same intermixture will be found. National defense requires adequate social measures for the control of atomic power.

This book is no place for predictions on the possible future uses of this new source of energy. The applications of new power supplies lie in the province of engineering, not physics. Unfortunately, in uranium alone, according to rough estimates, enough energy is available only to supply the power needs of this country for two hundred years. Before we can even afford nuclear power, the process will have to be made much cheaper. From the size of the piles described, it can be seen that we are still some distance from nuclear power for airplanes and automobiles. It may well be that other elements besides uranium will serve as a source of nuclear energy. Much work probably remains to be done, but it seems apparent that nuclear energy will become available at least on a power house scale.

One by-product of the pile will be production of radioactive isotopes on a scale hitherto unknown. Immediately the prospects of their use in biological research, and in medicinal healing, as already described, will be vastly enhanced. New physical tools will probably become available, and as further information is released the whole field of nuclear physics can be expected to respond to this new stimulus.

Still it is by no means clear that the vast amount of nuclear knowledge, apart from the technology of the bomb, which has been assembled in the course of these projects will be published and made available to physicists. It is unfortunately not even clear that we will retain freedom of research in investigating the basic nature of matter. Certainly no better method of stultifying progress in this country, both scientific and technological, could be found than to retard research. Free, unhampered scientific research, supported by the Government, by industry, by universities, is a fundamental necessity. The atomic bomb and the prospects of atomic power are but milestones along the way. Atom smashing has uncovered one secret in the nucleus. Infinitely more remains to be done before we can truly understand the nature of matter. To achieve this important end, further free research is the only key.

GLOSSARY AND NOTES

GLOSSARY

Actinium emanation: A natural radioactive gas, a heavy element with atomic number 86, which decays with the emission of alpha particles. Its half life is 3.9 seconds. Sometimes called actinon.

Alpha particle: The doubly charged nucleus of the helium atom, with a physical mass of 4.0028. The alpha particle is given off in the radioactive decay of natural radioactive elements, and can be made artificially by stripping the two exterior electrons from an ordinary neutral helium atom. Should it recapture one electron, the alpha particle can exist singly charged.

Ampere: A unit of current, a quantity of electricity flowing per second. Named after the French physicist, André Marie Ampère.

Anode: The positive electrode, derived from the Greek, *anodos*, meaning "way up," the going-in place for electrons. In a discharge tube electrons leave the cathode and go in the general direction of the anode.

Atmospheric pressure: The pressure of the air around us; against a vacuum the pressure of the atmosphere is about 15 pounds per square inch. The force on the walls of a vacuum chamber from the air outside it is also 15 pounds per square inch, no negligible force when a vacuum apparatus as large as an atom smasher is constructed.

Atom: The smallest unit of an element which retains the characteristics of the element. An atom is a system composed of a charged nucleus and a number of electrons (whose number is given by the number of elementary charges on the nucleus) which travel in orbits about the nucleus.

Atomic bomb: A contrivance which utilises nuclear energy to produce a devastating explosion.

ATOMIC NUMBER: An integral number equal to the number of positive charges contained in the nucleus of an atom.

BARIUM: A heavy element, with atomic number 56 and chemical weight 137.36. Barium is metallic, soft and silvery, chemically similar to radium and also to calcium.

BEAM: A ray. A beam of particles is like a ray of light. Sometimes used in laboratory parlance without "of particles"; a cyclotron beam refers to the beam of particles formed in the cyclotron.

BEAM INTEGRATOR: A device, usually electrical, to record the total amount of a beam over a given period – for example, the total amount of beam that arrives at the cyclotron target in one hour.

BERYLLIUM: A light metallic element, but a tough one. Atomic number of 4 and chemical mass of 9.02.

BETA PARTICLE: An electron, usually one which is given off in the disintegration of radioactive elements. Can be produced artificially by accelerating ordinary electrons to the high speeds common to those beta particles ejected in radioactive disintegration.

BILLION: A large number. The American billion of one thousand million is meant.

BINDING ENERGY: The amount of energy given off when elementary particles come together to form a nucleus. This energy must be supplied again for the nucleus to disintegrate, hence it is the binding energy.

BOMBARDMENT: When a beam of high speed particles impinges on a target, the target is bombarded.

CADMIUM: A soft bluish-white metal, with atomic number 48, a powerful slow neutron absorber.

CATHODE: The negative electrode, derived from the Greek, *kathodos*, meaning "descent," a going-out place for the electrons which are given off from the cathode.

CHAIN REACTION: A self-propagating reaction. A reaction in which the disintegration of one element produces products which in turn disintegrate the next element, and so on.

CHARGE: A quantity of electricity. The ultimate indivisible charge is the charge of one electron, 4.80×10^{-10} electrostatic units.

CHEMICAL MASS: The mass of an element measured on the chemical scale. On this scale the chemical mass of oxygen is arbitrarily set as 16.0000 and all other masses are measured relative to that. Since chemical measurements can only be made on large numbers of atoms, the chemical mass is always an average mass.

CLOUD CHAMBER: One of the most important tools in modern nuclear physics, discovered by C. T. R. Wilson. It is possible to photograph the tracks charged particles leave behind them as they traverse a cloud chamber.

COLLIMATE: Physics jargon; to collimate is to form a column (not an etymological derivation). Strictly speaking, a collimated beam should have parallel edges, but in practice anything that can be called a beam is considered as collimated.

CONDENSER: An electrical device which has the property of storing charge.

CORPUSCULAR: Made up of particles, usually small.

COSMIC RAYS: Penetrating radiation, of great scientific interest, which has its origin beyond the earth. Cosmic rays, like alpha and other particles, as well as gamma rays, can be detected by the ionisation they produce. They possess the property of ejecting great numbers of electrons in their passage through matter.

COULOMB: A unit of charge. The charge on the electron is 1.60×10^{-19} coulombs (or 4.80×10^{-10} electrostatic units).

CRITICAL SIZE: No reaction can take place in a pile, or an atomic bomb, unless the mass of material is larger than a critical size. When critical size is achieved the neutron loss through the surface of the pile becomes unimportant.

CURRENT: When charge flows through a wire, there is a current in it.

CYCLOTRON: A machine commonly used to smash atoms.

DAUGHTER ELEMENT: When a naturally radioactive element disintegrates spontaneously, the product element is its daughter element.

DEE: The accelerating electrodes in the cyclotron are called dees because viewed from above they bear a faint resemblance to the letter "D."

DEFLECTOR: A special electrode is used in the cyclotron to deflect the beam from its normal path so that the accelerated particles impinge on a particular target. This electrode is the deflector.

DEUTERIUM: A heavy hydrogen atom, comprising a deuteron and an electron.

DEUTERON: A particle, the heavy hydrogen nucleus with physical mass 2.0142 and unit positive charge which is used as projectile in atom smashers.

DISCHARGE: When an electrode loses its charge, often by a spark, a discharge has passed. Lightning is a typical example of a discharge.

DISINTEGRATION: A break up, usually of an atom. An atom that has been smashed has been disintegrated.

ELECTRICAL FIELD: When two nearby electrodes are charged an electrical field exists between them, if the voltage is not the same on each electrode.

ELECTRICAL FIRE: Franklin's own name for electricity.

ELECTRODE: A charged conductor is an electrode. Most commonly electrodes are metals, as, for example, the metal electrodes which are sealed into glass discharge tubes.

ELECTROMETER: An instrument used to measure electrical charge or a change in electrical voltage.

ELECTRON: A small negative particle whose charge is the fundamental negative charge.

ELECTRON VOLT: A unit of energy: the energy acquired by one electron in falling through a potential difference of one volt is one electron volt.

ELECTROSCOPE: An instrument to measure electrical charge or voltage; an electroscope usually makes its measurement by the mutual repulsion of two similarly charged gold leaves, or some analogous system.

ELECTROSTATICS: The subject matter of electrostatics is electricity at rest. Although an electrostatic generator introduces movement into the system, it does it mechanically rather than electrically, and, once on the large sphere on the top of such a generator, the charge is almost at rest.

ELEMENT: A simple form of matter which can not chemically be turned into a simpler form. It used to be said that elements were forms of matter that could not be changed by any means into simpler forms. Unfortunately for the purposes of definition, atom smashing is the best violation of this once respected statement.

ENERGY: Something that can be converted into work.

ENERGY STATE: Atoms and nuclei exist in certain stable conditions — under such conditions their energy remains constant, and the atoms or nuclei are in specific energy states. Change from one energy state to a neighboring one requires the expenditure of work. It is one of the consequences of the theories of modern physics that the stable energy states are discrete.

FIELD FREE SPACE: Space in which there is neither an electric nor a magnetic field.

FILAMENT: The thin wire in a lamp bulb which is heated to incandescence by the passage of the current is a filament. Hot filaments also possess the power of giving off electrons which makes them especially valuable in radio tubes.

FISSION: A term applied to the energetic disintegration of uranium — borrowed from biology where it is commonly used in describing cell division. Reasonably apt description because the uranium nucleus breaks up usually into two parts of approximately equal size.

FLUORESCENT SCREEN: When a charged particle, commonly an alpha particle or a proton, impinges on a fluorescent screen, a bright star of light erupts. Each such star heralds the arrival of a single charged particle.

FREQUENCY: How often something happens. The frequency of light, or similar waves, is the number of times the top of a wave goes by per second.

GAMMA RAY: A non-corpuscular radiation, like light, or x-rays, or radio waves, which is commonly emitted in some radioactive transformations.

GEIGER COUNTER: An apparatus for registering the passage of charged particles through a specially prepared tube. The disturbance created by the particle is amplified within the tube until it can be registered audibly or mechanically.

GRAM: A unit of weight equal to 0.035 ounces.

GRATING: A grating is used to determine the wave-length of light, reflected from its surface. The surface is a smooth one, usually of metal, on which a large number of lines are ruled, accurately parallel and very close together.

GROUND: The earth – a source and sink of electrons. Because of its large capacity it is difficult to charge up the earth, consequently it is a standard reference point on all electrical systems. Two points which are grounded are connected to one another as thoroughly as though a wire ran from one to the other.

HALF-LIFE: Radioactive substances decay according to a simple exponential law. Their rate of decay is often measured by their half-life, the time it takes for half the atoms in a radioactive element to disintegrate.

HELIUM: A light gas, a chemically inactive element with atomic number 2 and chemical mass of 4.003.

Hydrogen: The lightest gas – an element. Ordinary hydrogen has an atomic number of 1 and a chemical mass of 1.008; heavy hydrogen, an isotope with the same atomic number but twice the weight, is also known. Cyclotrons usually use heavy hydrogen to provide bombarding particles.

Impulse generator: A machine for developing voltage as high as 10 million volts. Useful in testing insulators and providing exhibitions. Has also been used in nuclear research.

Insulate: Electrical insulation is provided by non-conductors of electricity, ranging from the rubber that insulates ordinary lamp-cords to the air which insulates Van de Graaff generators.

Ionisation chamber: A chamber in which the ionisation produced by the passage of charged particles is measured. The measurement indicates the number of charged particles that have penetrated the chamber.

Ionise: A neutral atom which has lost one or more of the electrons that revolve about the nucleus is ionised. These positively charged atoms are ions.

Isotope: Isotopes are atoms with the same atomic number but different atomic mass – atomic twins. All the isotopes of any element have the same chemical properties.

k: A mathematical symbol. In a pile, k is the ratio of new neutrons available for fission, produced per neutron shot into the pile. The necessary condition for a pile to operate is $k = 1.0$. In this book, k always refers to piles of infinite size.

Lattice: A regular structure containing lumps of uranium imbedded in a moderator.

Leak: The specialised use of this word is for an air leak, a small orifice, usually hidden in the most inaccessible part of the apparatus, which permits air to enter where none is desired.

Leukemia: A fatal disease, often associated with a great increase of the number of white corpuscles in the blood.

Leyden jar: A condenser, usually a jar coated on the inside and outside with metallic foil. A Leyden jar possesses the power of storing charge.

LINEAR ACCELERATOR: A high voltage machine – a cyclotron with the kinks removed. In the linear accelerator the particles are accelerated in a straight line by the repeated application of low voltage to a number of succeeding electrodes through which the particle passes.

LINEAR AMPLIFIER: An amplifier usually used to amplify the ionisation produced by alpha particles in a suitable chamber. With a linear amplifier, the measured output is directly proportional to the ionisation in the chamber.

MAGNETIC FIELD: Between the poles of a maget a magnetic field exists. The field is responsible for the attraction of articles by a magnet; in a cyclotron it is responsible for curling the paths of the particles into circular orbits.

MASS: Quantity of matter. Often used loosely for either chemical or physical mass.

MASS NUMBER: That whole number closest to the physical mass of an isotope, equal to the sum of the number of protons and neutrons in the nuclear.

MEGACYCLE: A unit of frequency, a megacycle is a million cycles per second.

MICROAMPERE: A unit of current equal to one millionth of an ampere.

MODERATOR: Material, often contained in a pile, which has the property of slowing down neutrons.

MOLYBDENUM: A hard, heat resistant, silver white metal. The element molybdenum has an atomic number of 42, and a chemical mass of 95.95.

MONOCHROMATIC: Made of a single color. Also used in x-rays, where monochromatic x-radiation is similar to a single color of light radiation A monochromatic beam has a single sharply defined wave length.

N UNIT: A unit for the measurement of neutrons, in an ionisation chamber of special construction. The value of an *n* unit is numerically equal to that of an *r* unit.

NEPTUNIUM: An element, not found in nature before 1939, with atomic number 93.

NEUTRON: A particle of physical mass 1.0090 and no charge, discovered by Chadwick in 1932.

NUCLEAR CHARGE: The charge on the nucleus of an atom, usually given in terms of the electronic charge. A nuclear charge of 3 means a positive charge on the nucleus three times the elementary electronic charge.

NUCLEUS: The center of the atom, its distinctive core, or kernel.

OSCILLOSCOPE: A sensitive instrument which registers electrical phenomena by the motion of a beam of electrons on a fluorescent screen. An especially sensitive instrument, because the electron beam is such a responsive pointer.

OXYGEN: A gaseous element of atomic number 8 and chemical mass 16.000. Dry oxygen is oxygen containing no water.

PARABOLA: A geometric curve – the intersection of a cone with a plane which cuts it parallel to its side is a parabola.

PARALLEL: Leyden jar condensers are connected in parallel when the outside coating of each condenser is connected to a common wire, and the inside coating of each to another common wire.

PARTICLE: A word of all work applied to anything which has mass, usually small.

PHYSICAL MASS: The mass of a particle compared to the mass of the oxygen isotope with weight arbitrarily assigned as 16.0000. Since there are other heavier isotopes of oxygen, the physical mass is not equal to the chemical mass, but is somewhat lighter.

PILE: A large structure built of uranium, or other fissionable material, and a moderator in such a way that a sustained chain reaction takes place with the spontaneous and controlled evolution of energy.

PLUTONIUM: An element, not found in nature before 1939, with atomic number 94.

POLE: In a bar or a horseshoe magnet, the poles are the two ends of the magnets. The maximum intensity of a magnetic field is at the poles.

POLONIUM: A radioactive element of atomic number 84, and approximate chemical mass of 210. Also called Radium F. Named Polonium by Madame Curie, its discoverer, after her native country.

POSITIVE RAY: Positive radiation made up of the positive ions that are found in a discharge through low pressure gas.

POSITRON: The positive electron, having a mass equal to that of the electron, and a charge of the same magnitude but differing in sign.

PROTON: The singly charged nucleus of light hydrogen, with physical mass of 1.0076.

R UNIT: A unit of ionisation used in the measurement of x-rays, named after Röntgen, the discoverer of x-rays.

RADIUM: A metallic radioactive element of atomic number 88 and chemical mass 226.05. Radium decomposes with the emission of alpha particles, yielding radon.

RADON: A radioactive gas, an element with atomic number 86, and chemical mass of 222. Radon gives off alpha particles.

RECTIFIER: An apparatus, commonly a radio tube, which converts alternating current into direct current. Rectifiers are like one way streets, permitting the current to pass in only one direction.

RESISTANCE: When the passage of electrical current through a conductor is hindered, the conductor has resistance. Copper has very low resistance, and a good insulator has very high resistance.

SCINTILLATION: A bright star-like eruption of light.

SERIES: Leyden jars are connected in series when the outer coating of one is connected to the inner coating of its neighbor.

SHIMS: In a cyclotron the magnetic field is adjusted by a tiresome operation, the interposition of thin pieces of iron, shims, between the magnet poles and the cyclotron tank.

SLOW NEUTRONS: Neutrons that have been bounced around in a large block of paraffin or a large tank of water lose most of their energy. When their velocity is comparable to that of the hydrogen atoms in the paraffin or water, the neutrons are called slow neutrons.

SPARK GAP: A gap between two electrodes, which may be bridged by a spark.

SPECTROSCOPE: An instrument used to analyse light. A beam of light entering a spectroscope is broken up by passage through a prism or reflection from a grating into its component colors, or wave lengths.

TAMPER: Material used in an atomic bomb which serves the double purpose of reflecting neutrons back into the bomb material, and holding the bomb together as long as possible before explosive rupture.

TANK: The cyclotron tank is the vacuum tight body which goes between the poles of the magnet, and contains dees, deflector, and target.

THORIUM: A radioactive element with atomic number 90, and chemical mass 232.12 – disintegrates with the emission of an alpha particle.

TRANSFORMER: A device which makes use of certain properties of alternating currents to multiply or divide the voltage in the circuit.

TRANSMUTATION: A change in the nucleus of an atom which is so great that the atom loses its identity and becomes a different atom.

URANIUM: A radioactive metal, the heaviest natural element known, with atomic number 92 and chemical mass 238.07.

Uranium emits alpha particles.

VACUUM: A desideratum in cyclotrons and other atom smashers. A good vacuum means a pressure about a hundred millionth that of the atmosphere outside.

VOLT: A unit of electrical potential. Loosely the voltage may be regarded as the pressure which pushes the current through a wire.

VOLTAGE DOUBLER: An atom smasher devised by Cockcroft and Walton which obtains its high voltage from a number of condensers and rectifiers connected in a special circuit.

WATT: A unit of power. Watts are computed by multiplying the voltage by the current in amperes.

WAVE LENGTH: The wave length is the distance between the top of one wave and the top of the next succeeding one.

X-RAY: A non-corpuscular radiation, similar to light.

ZINC SULPHIDE SCREEN: A screen coated with zinc sulphide is fluorescent and gives off scintillations when struck by a heavy charged particle, like an alpha particle or proton.

NOTES

CHAPTER 1

The value of the charge of the electron is 4.80×10^{-10} electrostatic units, and its mass 9.035×10^{-28} grams.

Further account:

J. J. Thomson, *Philosophical Magazine*, series 5, vol. 44 (1897), p. 293.

R. A. Millikan, *Electrons (+ and −), Protons, Photons, Neutrons, and Cosmic Rays* (Chicago, 1935), Chapters 1, 2, 3, and 4.

CHAPTER 2

The mass of the proton is 1.6609×10^{-24} grams.

Further account:

J. J. Thomson, Bakerian lecture, *Proceedings of the Royal Society*, vol. A 89 (1913), p. 1.

F. W. Aston, *Mass-Spectra and Isotopes* (London, 1933), Chapters 3 and 5.

CHAPTER 3

The mass of the neutron is 1.6622×10^{-24} grams.

Further account:

James Chadwick, Bakerian lecture, *Proceedings of the Royal Society*, vol. A 142 (1933), p. 1.

CHAPTER 4

Further account:

Rutherford, *Philosophical Magazine*, series 6, vol. 21 (1911), p. 669.

Hans Geiger and E. Marsden, *Philosophical Magazine*, series 6, vol. 25 (1913), p. 604.

CHAPTER 5

Further account:

H. G. J. Moseley and C. G. Darwin, *Philosophical Magazine*, series 6, vol. 26 (1913), p. 210.

H. G. J. Moseley, *Philosophical Magazine*, series 6, vol. 26 (1913), p. 1024.

H. G. J. Moseley, *Philosophical Magazine*, series 6, vol. 27 (1914), p. 703.

CHAPTER 6

Einstein's equation for the equivalence of mass and energy is $E = mc^2$, where E is the energy, m the mass, and c the velocity of light. One mass unit is equivalent to 931 million electron volts, and the mass of the proton is equivalent to 938 million electron volts.

Further account:

Hans Bethe and R. F. Bacher, *Reviews of Modern Physics*, vol. 8 (1936), p. 83, paragraphs 1 and 2.

Further references are Rutherford's Bakerian lecture, and *The Newer Alchemy*, given more especially for Chapter 7.

CHAPTER 7

Further account:

Rutherford, Bakerian lecture, *Proceedings of the Royal Society*, vol. A 97 (1920), p. 374.

Rutherford, *The Newer Alchemy* (Cambridge, 1937), for this and succeeding chapters.

James Chadwick, *Radioactivity and Radioactive Substances* (London, 1932), Chapters 1, 4, 5, and 6.

CHAPTER 8

Further account:

J. D. Cockcroft and E. T. S. Walton, *Proceedings of the Royal Society*, vol. A 136 (1932), p. 619.

J. D. Cockcroft and E. T. S. Walton, *Proceedings of the Royal Society*, vol. A 137 (1932), p. 229.

CHAPTER 9

Further account:

R. J. Van de Graaff, K. T. Compton, and L. C. Van Atta, *Physical Review*, vol. 43 (1933), p. 149.

CHAPTER 10

Further account:

E. O. Lawrence and M. S. Livingston, *Physical Review*, vol. 40 (1932), p. 19.

E. O. Lawrence and D. Cooksey, *Physical Review*, vol. 50 (1936), p. 1131.

CHAPTER 11

Further account:

Rutherford and Hans Geiger, *Proceedings of the Royal Society*, vol. A 81 (1908), p. 141.

James Chadwick, *Radioactivity and Radioactive Substances*, Chapters 2 and 3.

John Strong, *Procedures in Experimental Physics* (New York, 1939), Chapter 7.

CHAPTER 12

Further account:

C. T. R. Wilson, *Philosophical Transactions*, vol. A 189 (1897), p. 265.

C. T. R. Wilson, *Philosophical Transactions*, vol. A 192 (1899), p. 403.

CHAPTER 13

Further account:

L. A. Turner, *Reviews of Modern Physics*, vol. 12 (1940), p. 1.

CHAPTER 14

Further account:

M. S. Livingston and Hans Bethe, *Reviews of Modern Physics*, vol. 9 (1937), p. 245.

CHAPTER 15

Further account:

John Lawrence, *Handbook of Physical Therapy*, American Medical Association, 3rd ed. (Chicago, 1939), p. 438.

D. M. Greenberg, *Annual Review of Biochemistry* (1939), p. 269.

CHAPTERS 16, 17, AND 18

Further account:

H. D. Smyth, *Atomic Energy for Military Purposes* (Princeton University Press, 1945). Also available from Superintendent of Documents, United States

Government Printing Office, Washington, D.C. This is the authoritative source on which these chapters were based. Released by the government, it is written in semitechnical language.

The eye-witness account of the explosion is taken from the first of a series of articles in the New York *Times* by William Laurence.

General

The Bakerian lectures are usually less complex than original papers, for they are delivered by invitation before the Royal Society after the particular research has been once reported. Rutherford's 1920 Bakerian lecture is one of the classics of modern physics. Often, however, the original reports give the most lucid explanation of the experiments; Moseley's papers are outstanding for their clarity.

Besides the history of electricity, Millikan's book on the electron offers an interesting account of the discovery of the positron (Chapter XIV). There are many good books about radioactivity — Rutherford, Chadwick, and Ellis's *Radiations from Radioactive Substances* is a standard reference for physicists. Chadwick's little book is more an introduction to it, while Rutherford's *The Newer Alchemy* is a good popular book. *Ions, Electrons, and Ionizing Radiations* by J. A. Crowther (London, 7th ed., 1938) is an excellent text book to supplement a beginner's knowledge.

In modern nuclear physics, there is no such wealth of books, although most of those mentioned in connection with radioactivity treat nuclear physics in more or less detail. For the physicist, two articles in the *Review of Modern Physics*, one by Bethe and Bacher (vol. 8, 1936, p. 83) and one by Livingston and Bethe (vol. 9, 1937, p. 245), provide an excellent detailed account.

J. J. Thomson's *Recollections and Reflections* (New York, 1937) is a delightful autobiography that makes excellent reading. The most authoritative account of Rutherford is A. S. Eve's *Rutherford* (New York, 1939), especially interesting for the many quotations from Rutherford's letters. Finally, the changing relation between science and society is brilliantly examined by J. D. Bernal in *The Social Function of Science* (London, 1939).

INDEX

INDEX

The abbreviation Gl. following a page number shows that the reference is to the Glossary.